Illustrations by
Siegfried Kaden

Introduction by
Jorge Castellanos

Markus Wiener
Publishers
PRINCETON

AFRO-CUBAN MYTHS

Yemayá and Other Orishas

Rómulo Lachatañeré

Translated from Spanish by
Christine Ayorinde

For information write to:
Markus Wiener Publishers, 231 Nassau Street, Princeton, NJ 08542

Book design by Cheryl Mirkin

Library of Congress Cataloging-in-Publication Data

Lachatañeré, R. (Rómulo)
    [Oh, mío Yemayá!! English]
    Afro-Cuban myths : Yemayá and other orishas / Rómulo Lachatañeré ;
translated from the Spanish by Christine Ayorinde.
    ISBN 1-55876-317-1 (hc. : alk. paper)
    ISBN 1-55876-318-X (pb.)
    I. Ayorinde, Christine. II. Title.
PQ7389.I23O513 2003
398.2'097291—dc22
2003059619

Printed in the United States of America on acid-free paper

Contents

Introduction by Jorge Castellanos
Rómulo Lachatañeré:
Pioneer of Afro-Cuban Studies • vii
Reference Notes • xvii

Agayú Solá • 1

The River • 3

Aché • 7

Punishment • 9

Destiny • 13

The Ekuelé Divining Tray • 17

The Revelation • 19

Forgetfulness • 24

Covetousness • 29

Changó • 35

Oyá • 37

The Obeyes • 42

Incest • 60

Oba • 63

Ochún • 69

Echú and the Pumpkin • 71

Orúmbila's Parrots • 77

The Sacrifice • 82

Ogún Arere's Traps • 86

Deception • 91

Yemayá • 99
Orisaoco • 101

Ogún Arere • 107
Cunning • 109

Ochosi de Mata • 113
Ochosi de Mata • 115

Orúmbila • 123
Orúmbila's Moquenquen • 125
Orúmbila and Icú • 130

Songs or Prayers of the Güemilere • 133

Vocabulary • 145

About the Contributors • 154

# INTRODUCTION
Rómulo Lachatañeré:
Pioneer of Afro-Cuban Studies[1]

When speaking of the origins of Afro-Cuban studies in Cuba, two famous names are always mentioned, and quite rightly: those of Fernando Ortiz and Lydia Cabrera. But that of another pioneer, whose work is seminal in the development of Creole ethnology, is systematically forgotten: Rómulo Lachatañeré.

Lachatañeré, whose surname is a hispanicised form of the French surname Lachataignerais, was born in Santiago de Cuba in 1909. He came from one of those distinguished Oriente mulatto families who have made such an important contribution to the political, economic, and cultural life of the country. (He was a grandson of Flor Crombet.) He completed his early education in his native city and then graduated in pharmacy from the University of Havana. He lived for a time in Manzanillo and finally moved to New York, where he worked in the laboratory of Columbia University Hospital. He died in a plane crash in Puerto Rico in 1952.

His book *Oh mio Yemaya!*,[2] published in Manzanillo in 1938, was the first attempt in Cuba to gather a sizeable sample of the numerous *patakíes* or myths characteristic of the *Regla de Ocha* or Santería, the most widespread of the Afro-Cuban cults practiced on the island. In the prologue, Fernando Ortiz refers to the serious obstacles the author was obliged to overcome in order to perform his task. In the first place, he had to battle against the prejudice that considered the Afro-Cuban religion and its associated literature to be undeserving of intellectual attention. "In the same way that the musicians who composed *habaneras* would deny the negroid flow of their erotic sweetness even when they carried it in their own blood... the literati deemed it preferable to glorify and romanticize the long extinct Indians, while despising the blacks who lived alongside them. For them, that descent into the crypt of African mysteries in order to capture the poetic content of their liturgies and myths was despicable and socially and even religiously sinful."[3]

But there was more: it was necessary to penetrate the secrecy in which black believers cloaked their beliefs and their cults, fearful—with good reason—of attracting all manner of disdain, desecration and persecution. To the arrogance of the dominant culture was added the understandable inferiority complex of the subjugated culture. Exorcising those demons was not a simple matter.

Added to all this was the oral nature of the mythological tradition, first in Africa and then in Cuba. The myths of Santería, transported in the minds of the slaves, reached the island in the Yoruba language. They underwent a process of transculturation parallel to that of the language. The myths formed part of the divination system and were recounted in such a way that they could be understood by those believers who were gradually losing fluency in their ancestral tongue. It is likely that they were orally translated first into *bozal* and then into the often incorrect and simplistic Spanish in which they appear today in the *libretas* or holy books of the *santeros*. In the end it was necessary to put them into standard Spanish.

The problem was not merely a linguistic one. With the passing of the centuries, those myths were eroded, telescoped and acquired all manner of extraneous accretions, often to the point of becom-

Rómulo Lachatañeré
(Self-portrait ca. 1950s)

ing unintelligible. Lachatañeré gathered almost all the *patakíes* from an *iyalocha* (or santera) in Regla. His work was not only to "translate" them but also give them a suitably literary form without betraying their basic meaning or feeling, that is without "whitening" or "westernizing" their Afro-Cubanness to the point where it is completely distorted. A huge problem neatly solved. Armed only with his common sense and a love of truth and tradition, the author manages to lend his work complete authenticity, facilitating the interpretative work of later ethnologists and folklorists. *Oh, mio Yemaya!* is a Cuban classic, found only with great difficulty in a few North American libraries and which, let it be stressed, demands a speedy reissue.

This book contains 21 legends or *patakíes* in the form of "stories" reassembled by Lachatañeré. In them we do not find the metaphorical pyrotechnics and overflowing imagination of those by Lydia Cabrera.[4] But some attain a very considerable level of artistry, as is the case of the lyrical story about Oba (wife of Changó) and the poignant loss of her beauty. Others, which tell of the life and miracles of the major orichas, in particular Changó, Ochún, Yemayá, and Ogún, are extremely valuable sources for the study of Lucumí mythology. For example, *Orúmbila's Parrots*, which tells of Ochún's adultery with Ogún Arere, is a fable comparable to those of Venus and Jupiter. The divine protagonists of some of these pieces recall others from the Graeco-Roman pantheon such as Mars, Vulcan, and Hercules, though without losing their Africanity and typically Creole sense of mischief.

In an effort to remain true to his oral sources, Lachatañeré's style is straightforward, simple and unadorned. Nicolás Guillén finds in this work by his good friend "more than one wonderfully successful page" and even when he notes a certain faltering in others, according to him they are always saved by "the charm, the enchantment of the fable, the naivety of the plot, lacking in any literary artifice and which manages through its essential force to make an impact."[5] Perhaps it is for this very reason that these tales are so moving. They lead us directly, without detours, into a marvelous and magical world—the numinous imagination of Afro-Cubans, which represents their elemental and profound response to fundamental questions of popular and universal theology and philosophy.

In his next publication, an essay entitled "The religious system of the Lucumís and other African influences in Cuba," Lachatañeré establishes the methodological and semantic routes to be followed by subsequent Cuban ethnology. He highlights the outstanding merit of Fernando Ortiz's groundbreaking work. He declares himself a disciple while not hesitating to point out his teacher's mistakes and limitations. Ortiz, with the greatness characteristic of truly wise men, accepts this serenely, publishing the work of his critic in the pages of the journal *Estudios Afrocubanos*, which he edited. That generous creative collaboration—so rare in Cuba—enabled the rapid advance of Afro-Cuban studies at a crucial point in their development.[6]

Lachatañeré gets to the bottom of the problem. He explains that the focus of the early work of Ortiz was strictly penological. His study of blacks is a study of the black "underworld." Influenced by Lombroso and Ferri, in Afro-Cuban culture he sees only the supposed atavism of the "primitive peoples" brought to Cuba by the slave trade. Lachatañeré proposes a strictly anthropological approach based on existing methods of scientific ethnology. Ortiz's corrections (already begun of his own accord) and the research of Lydia Cabrera soon proved how fertile this new approach would be.

Navigating the dense jungle of the innumerable African ethnicities found in Cuba with a sure compass, he established clear boundaries between the cultural complexes produced by transculturation. As he explained, in Cuba there are three main ones: the Lucumí, of Yoruba origin; the Congo, of Bantu provenance; and the Carabalí, from Calabar. Each has a distinct religious system associated with it: the *Regla de Ocha* of the Lucumís, *Palomonte* or *Mayombe* (in all its varieties) of the Congos; the Abakuá Secret Society (*ñáñigos*) of the Carabalíes. Up until that point the Afro-Cuban beliefs were generally regarded as an impenetrable tangle of heterogeneous elements lumped together under the heading of *brujería* [witchcraft]. This streamlined classification made possible the systematic and "neutral" (that is, unprejudiced) study of each culture and religion.[7]

Lachatañeré was opposed to the use of the term "witchcraft" to describe the Afro-Cuban beliefs, quite rightly considering it discriminatory. He noted that even in Africa during the period of the slave trade, the "sorcerer" was always regarded as an anti-social and subversive agent. "In African societies the sorcerer is always considered an unnatural being whose criminal acts deserve every condemnation. They were severely punished with the death penalty and in fact it was the priests who were given the task of judging them."[8] The African slaves brought that concept of the criminal nature of witchcraft with them to Cuba.

Afflicted with an intense ethnocentrism, the colonial authorities and also those of the early Republic confused strictly religious practices with those that were black magic or harmful and they persecuted them all equally. This is why labelling the *reglas congas* or the *regla lucumí* "witchcraft" was profoundly racist. Those who confused them with criminality and with the underworld turned hundreds of thousands of practitioners into common habitual criminals and their devotional rites and mystical beliefs into concepts of criminal law.

Also discriminatory and unscientific, according to the author of this study, was the use of the term *brujo* or *fetichero* to designate those who were merely priests of perfectly legitimate religious cults. One must call them by their names, insists Lachatañeré, *santeros* or *santeras*, or more specifically and according to their hierarchies, *babalaos*, *babalochas*, or *iyalochas* in the *Regla de Ocha*, and *mayomberos* or *nganguleros* in *palo*. *Brujos* or *brujas* are "the priests or priestesses or those outside of the priesthood who display a preference for the practices of black magic, using the aforementioned concept as it is used in African societies."[9] In this way, the practices relating to negative or harmful magic and muddled popular superstitions are neatly and permanently separated from the authentic *religions* that are the Afro-Cuban *reglas*.

Lachatanere accepts that, among the huge mass of humanity cast onto the island by the slave traders, some *brujos* (in the African sense of the word) must surely have reached Cuba and practiced their ancestral rites there. He notes that "among the aforementioned slaves there were *brujos* and criminals who must for a time have continued their villainous way of life, especially on the sugar plantations where the isolation and oppression offered plenty of opportunity for those who had been outside the law in their own land to continue their excesses in that terrible setting. But these are criminal cases that should be classified outside of the study of religion."[10]

Another seminal contribution of this work is the distinction drawn between two phases of the economic process and, therefore, of the slavery regime in Cuba, resulting from the upsurge in sugar plantations in the late eighteenth century. As we have noted elsewhere, Cuban slavery cannot be fully understood without studying the differences between the pre-plantation and plantation society insofar as they form two distinct, if interrelated, social and servile systems. It is this fundamental concept that allows a fuller understanding of the historical background of Afro-Cuban culture from colonial times up until the Republic.[11]

Lachatañeré studied the Afro-Cuban religions at both extremes of the island. In his essay he notes that the *Regla de Ocha* predominates in Havana and Matanzas, while in Santiago de Cuba and Guantánamo, although Santería is found, it is eclipsed by the *reglas congas*. Everything seems to indicate that interpenetration or "crossing" between the two sects is more acute there than in the capital. These religious differences between the west and the east of Cuba have never been given the attention they merit. More than half a century later, Lachatañeré's work is still suggesting virgin themes for a new generation of researchers.

In 1942, Editorial Caribe published *Manual de Santería: el sistema de los cultos lucumis* [*Manual of santería: the system of the Lucumí cults*] in which our author attempts the first panoramic, organic and systematic view of an Afro-Cuban religion. From the preface onwards, a new orientation is evident, a new methodology: to present the beliefs in keeping with the practitioners' own views, without first making them pass through the filter of anthropological theory. "Our intention," writes Lachatañeré, "is to attempt to present the beliefs under discussion in accordance with the interpretations of Afro-Cubans, discounting any judgment that stems from our intellect, . . . putting the Afro-Cubans themselves on stage . . . allowing them to act."[12] This is precisely the method that would be followed shortly afterwards by Lydia Cabrera, the most prolific researcher in this field: reproducing what her informants told her almost verbatim and with a minimum of organization and thus making her books true primary sources of ethnographic material.

The *Manual* makes a fruitful methodological contribution by insisting on treating the island's three Afro-Cuban religious systems separately, though Lachatañeré makes the mistake of giving the term Santería a generic sense to include them all. In fact, the name Santería should be applied only to the *Regla de Ocha*. However, the work does point out the main differences between it, *palo monte* or *mayombe*, and *ñáñiguismo* without omitting to also note areas of convergence between the three religious complexes.

Here Lachatañeré offers the first systematic study in Cuba of the *orichas* or *santos* [saints] who give the *Regla Ocha* its popular name of Santería. He gives detailed descriptions of the worship of Ochún, Yemayá, Changó, Eleguá, Ogún, Babalú Ayé, etc., as well as the different "paths" or advocations of each. He notes their syncretic nature: the fusion with saints of the Catholic Church. But he suggests that this system is not strictly polytheist, since a personal supreme creator god—omnipotent and omnipresent if also distant and "in retirement"—called Olorun, Olodumare, Olofi or Olofin rules over these deities.

Much less useful is the study of the liturgy offered by the *Manual*. The author appears to have had very limited access to Santería ceremonies. He speaks of the *asiento* or initiation but without going into detail. The same applies to the sacrifices, the "spells," possession, the *tambor* or güemilere [drum ceremony], the *ituto* or funerary rites etc. But the scheme is in place, attracting the attention of researchers. The priestly hierarchies (the distinction between *babalaos*, *babalochas*, *iyalochas*, etc.) are clearly defined.

The ritual best described is the oracle or divination system known as *Dilogún*, which is performed using 16 shells called cowries. Lachatañeré gives a detailed description of the system of prediction, its *odus*, "letters" or "signs," and the *patakíes* or myths associated with them. Nevertheless, there is very little in the book on the three other divination systems: *coco* (also called *Obi* or *Biagué*), the *Ifá* divining tray, and the *Ekuele*. The final chapter of the book is devoted to *brujería*. Here he develops what he had outlined previously in the article published in *Estudios Afrocubanos*. Finally, he includes a very useful table of the Lucumí deities, an equally important selection of salutations to the saints in Cuban Yoruba and of the verses recited when each letter of the Dilogún is thrown.

The *Manual de santeria* is undoubtedly a work of limited range, but no other had systematized, as it does, everything that was known at the time about Afro-Cuban religions. Fernando Ortiz and Lydia Cabrera continued to research and write until they were well advanced in years; Lachatañeré died at the age of 42. He did not have time to do all he would surely have been able to. But what he did is enough to place his name among the great pioneers of ethnological research in his country. "He cleaned, fixed and put a shine on" studies that, before his arrival, suffered from methodological and semantic confusion. He put things in order, he clarified, he classified, he compiled material, he blazed trails, he pointed out directions, he proposed themes. What more could one ask of him?

Jorge Castellanos

Notes to the Introduction

1. An expanded version of this introductory essay appears in *Pioneros de la etnografía afrocubana: Fernando Ortiz, Rómulo Lachatañeré, Lydia Cabrera* (Miami: Ediciones Universal, 2003).

2. This title is another example of the problems that arise when attempting to transcribe an unknown language. The author should have written *Omí o Yemayá!*—an *anagó* (the language of the Cuban Lucumís) ritual phrase meaning "You, water, Yemayá!" that refers to that goddess's characterization as the queen of the seas.

3. Ortiz, in Lachatañeré, *Oh, mío Yemayá*, p. xiv.

4. Although both authors are writing narrative, they have different intentions. Lachatañeré is attempting to reproduce the *pataki* exactly; Cabrera gives free rein to her creative imagination and liberally adapts material of Afro-Cuban or other origin though she interprets it in keeping with the spirit of that culture. Lachatañeré's intention is basically ethnographic; in her *Cuentos*, that of Cabrera is mainly literary.

5. Nicolás Guillén, *Prosa de Prisa* (Buenos Aires, 1968), p. 172.

6. Rómulo Lachatañeré, "El sistema religioso de los lucumís y otras influencias africanas en Cuba," *Estudios Afrocubanos* 3, nos. 1–4 (1939): 28–90; 4, nos. 1–4 (1940): 27–38; 5 (1945–46): 190–215.

7. Lydia Cabrera had already intuited these differences before the appearance of Lachatañeré's works. In her early stories, published in Paris in 1936, even those that are not *patakíes* but the product of her shimmering imagination, she never confuses Lucumi with Congo or Abakuá. Fernando Ortiz in his early works also shows that he is aware of the specific roles played by the descendants of the Yoruba, the Congo, and the Carabalí in Cuba. Lachatañeré's achievement was mainly in defining, conceptualizing, and systematizing the basic Afro-Cuban cultural complexes.

8. Lachatañeré, art. cit., *Estudios Afrocubanos* 3 (1939): 78.

9. Ibid., 77.

10. Ibid., 81–82.

11. Cf. Jorge and Isabel Castellanos, *Cultura Afrocubana*, vols. 1 and 2, esp. chapter 2 of the first volume.

12. Rómulo Lachatañeré, *Manual de Santería: el sistema de cultos lucumís* (Havana, 1942), p. 10.

Reference Notes

The legends that inspired the stories in this volume were collected in Havana City, where I spent most of my time. Visiting the places where santero rituals were celebrated, I was able to establish close friendships with some professionals of the Yoruba cult and to delve into the folkloric details and meaning of this engaging form of superstition.

I cultivated the friendship of a sweet young woman, a good person who was full of spontaneous fervor for the religion of her ancestors, to the point where I became her close confidant. It was she who told me most of these stories.

My brief stay in Manzanillo has had no influence on the publication of these pages. Where there is a black person there is *brujería*.[1] This is a sign that must be followed, and in this area of Manzanillo and Bayamo there are not many black people apart from sporadic, not very significant traces. These areas are the center of a type of popular spiritism that is deeply rooted in the spirit of the people and which they call *olilé*—some say this word is a corruption of the Yoruba term *olelé*, meaning a kind of maize pancake—which I understand harks back to the *miserere* of the early Catholics.

In Santiago de Cuba and Guantánamo, important urban centres with a significant number of blacks, the Yoruba religion is practiced with slight variations—a mixture of Lucumí and Congo rites. *Brujería* is practiced in the predominantly black areas of Alto Songo and San Luis, but I have not ascertained what form it takes.

In Matanzas there are numerous cabildos. In some districts, such as Alacranes and Colón, the ritual has retained all of its purity and the religious fervor with which the proselytes devote themselves to their practices makes me inclined to think they are the most holy and sacred places of the Yoruba cult in Cuba.

In Havana City, on nights when the feasts of important saints are celebrated, from every rambling old house inhabited by black people will come the melancholy lament of the drums seeping out through its doors; restless rhythms of hope and charity for these people's difficult lives. The cult has left indelible traces in Regla, a suburb close to the great city that was formerly a depository of freed slaves but now whitened, as out of necessity, Afro-Cubans have migrated to the large urban centers. It has been preserved with evident vitality, though it has to some extent lost its mystical sense. The same thing occurs in Guanabacoa and the spreading neighborhoods of Havana.

Lastly, I would hope this volume may serve to stimulate others, with more discipline and a greater capacity for hard work than I, to incorporate the black—very much a part of my flesh—into the national culture.

Agayú Solá

# The River

The hordes of men advanced deep into the impenetrable forest, savagely tearing down the dense trees, trampling the green grass that grew on the paths and pulling up by the roots the slender bushes that blocked their destructive impulse. They built roads. Narrow paths carpeted with fallen leaves appeared that gave way to wide roads skirting the high and inaccessible mountains that rose to meet their natural ceiling: the sky.

In this way man created his communication routes and extended the boundaries of the villages, establishing new links and taking possession of more and more of the forest's jealously guarded secrets. In the wildest and densest part of the forest where the harshness of the terrain curbed man's audacity, the river flowed, majestic and menacing. From the highest plateaus it could be seen meandering through the mountains like a silvery monster that moves forward sluggishly. But when the distance was covered in a determined effort, the river, seen from nearby, revealed all its fury, its choppy water, its raging eddies rising, writhing like a wounded serpent rippling its back in the throes of death. The river roared lugubriously, a thunderous and menacing sound. Even the bravest hearts were filled with awe, and no one dared risk the dangerous undertaking of conquering the current.

When all the others had left, convinced that any attempt to conquer the river would be fruitless, Agayú Solá, a farmer who was elderly but as strong and vigorous as a young warrior and irascible and hardworking, stood beside it looking at it defiantly. After thinking for a moment, he took his sharp axe and began to cut down a huge tree. Its trunk was so wide that it could not comfortably be encircled by the arms of five people. When he had finally felled it, he stripped away the branches with his battle machete. He made a bonfire whose sputtering flames rose, illuminating the sky with its bright sparks.

Then he let a slow fire bore through the resinous trunk of the felled tree while he shaped the wood until he had fashioned a crude boat. He made two powerful oars out of the same wood. When he considered his work done, he put some provisions in his boat and set out on his adventure. He rowed, cutting through the current, beating it tirelessly with his oars. The river put up a resistance equal to that of a thousand animals pulling in the same direction. But Agayú Solá cut through the river in his small boat. All his muscles flexed, and the veins on his neck stood out, his chest expanding and contracting like an accordion. The oars hit the water, *thwack, thwack, thwack*. The river raged furiously, *rrr rrr*. Rocking wildly, the boat moved forward. Agayú inched forward. Every inch gained was one less opportunity for the river to swallow him and his boat. The daring boatman rowed more swiftly though the current that gradually became less strong.

Once he had covered half the distance, Agayú gathered strength and, with odd movements, he broke through the current, making the boat move forward rapidly until it reached the opposite bank of the river. He leaped ashore and, rubbing his hands together, said: "I have conquered you; now I will finish you off."

Without pausing for breath, he climbed into the boat again and crossed the river, this time with much less effort than in the first contest.

Agayú Solá did this ten times until he turned the river into a calm, quiet stream on which the boat glided slowly and smoothly. Thanks to Agayú 's efforts, contact was established between the villages that had the river as their boundary. In return for his achievement, anyone who wanted to cross over to the other side had to pay a fee to the farmer who had become a boatman. He also became a wealthy man.

One day a woman arrived on the riverbank. Dressed in a voluminous coarse woollen cloth, she had a beautiful face and good manners. She climbed into the boat, indicating to the boatman that he should take her to the other side. When he saw her distinguished appearance, Agayú thought it prudent not to mention the fee for his work. Settling her comfortably in his boat, he began to row. When they reached the bank, the woman jumped up and began patiently arranging the folds of her skirt, scarcely looking at the boatman. This gave Agayú an opportunity to claim his payment. "Omordé,[5] pay me the fee."

The woman responded by taking off her dress and lying down on the grass. Agayú, seeing her thus, mounted her, and they had sexual intercourse. Afterwards the woman said: "You have had the great honor of sleeping with Obatalá." And she disappeared, leaving the boatman bewildered.

And that was that.

# Aché

Without knowing it, Agayu Solá had possessed Obatalá, the most powerful woman among those lares, who had the gift of being able to transform her appearance. Sometimes she appeared in the guise of a humble and gentle lover, sometimes in that of a warrior full of fighting spirit, able to perform valiant deeds, giving orders arrogantly, and treating her enemies ruthlessly. But this one adventure had not satisfied the ferryman. He felt his manhood humiliated. He needed to find out who Obatalá was. He thought that the most proper thing would have been for him to make the first move as men usually do. That is why he changed his manner toward those who came to cross the river. To each one that came he said: "Who are you and where do you come from?"

And they had to answer: "I am so-and-so."

"Well, pay me the fee."

"Here it is."

If this procedure was not followed, Agayú Solá would fold his arms and remain deaf to all requests. When anyone insisted he would say: "Find a name and a coin and you may cross the river; otherwise you are just a miserable timewaster."

Lo and behold one day a child appears before him and says:

"Agayu Solá, I want to go and see my mother who is on the other side."

"What is your name, moquenquen?"[7]

"I don't have a name."

"Well, in that case I can't help you."

The child began to cry and retorted: "It's been a long time since I saw my iyare;[8] perhaps after this I may never see her again. Take me."

"How many coins do you have?"

"I am very poor."

Then the ferryman answered: "Moquenquen, go back to where you came from. I cannot violate my principles."

"Then carry me on your shoulders. You have never said 'I will charge you so much for carrying you on my shoulders.'"

"You are smart; I will carry you," said Agayú, lifting the child and entering the river. But as soon as he began to walk he noticed that the child grew heavier and heavier until he was an unbearable weight. "What the hell is making you so heavy?" Agayú asked him, struggling to keep him on his shoulder.

"Don't ask questions, and keep your word."

"Moquenquen, I can't go on."

"Then look at me!"

The ferryman turned his face toward the child and cried out, letting him fall into the water. "Odu-dua!"

The child, floating on the water, came up to him and said: "For your efforts, I hand the river over to you."

Then he disappeared. And that was that.

 # Punishment

After her meeting with Agayú Solá, Obatalá assumed the avatar of Osan-quiriñán[9] and climbed the peaks leading to her snowy white ilé.[10] There she devoted herself to her duties, not attaching any importance to her fleeting adventure. Soon afterward she felt the discomfort that precedes motherhood. But the woman did not worry, and she continued to be absorbed in her tasks. Until one day she felt very intense pains, as if something was trying to escape from her insides.

Obatalá said: "I will push until it comes out."

Soon after, a child emerged. The woman who had just given birth took him in her arms and stroking him, said: "You will be called Changó."

"I like that name," said the moquenquen.

After this, Obatalá returned to her affairs and did not take any notice of the moquenquen. He got bored and ran from one end of the house to the other, or he remained lying on the floor, his eyes fixed on the dome of sky for long stretches of time. When he saw his mother coming, he clutched at her, hugging her legs, and asked with tears in his eyes: "Obatalá, who is my father?"

"I don't know, moquenquen; don't pester me!"

Changó wept. "Waah, waah, waah . . ." And he detached himself from his mother, dragging his little legs along the ground, very distressed and sad.

On the following day he said to his mother again: "Obatalá, I want to see my father!"

"Moquenquen, I don't have time to answer you."

And every day it was the same: "My iyare, I want to see my father!"

Until one day Obatalá, fed up, replied: "It's Agayú Solá; go and stay with him!" She had barely finished her sentence when Changó swiftly escaped, sliding down the mountains like a gazelle. He disappeared into the forest, shouting: "Agayú Solá! Agayú Solá!"

It so happened that Agayú Solá still remembered the woman. He thought about her every afternoon, and he would go into the forest, stricken with an inexplicable rage. He walked so quickly that he left trees swaying in his wake. He wept copious tears that beat heavily on the dry leaves scattered on the ground. And the forest was filled with sadness. The afternoons went by slowly and monotonously, for Agayú Solá was so affected by the memory of the woman that he lost all sense of time.

That afternoon he heard the child's voice calling out his name, and he stopped in the bend of a path to wait for him.

"What are you looking for, moquenquen?"

"I'm looking for my father."

"And you, who are you?"

"I'm Babá's[11] child."

When he heard this, Agayú trembled with rage and asked him again: "Who is your father?"

"You are."

Then Agayú said: "Moquenquen, I am far too hungry to listen to all your nonsense. I will roast you, and you will do me for a meal."

Changó did not turn a hair and said to him, smiling: "You will not kill me; you are my father."

"No? Wait and see."

Agayú took some branches, piled them up, and set them alight. He began to stoke up the fire in front of the impassive boy, who had not stopped smiling. When the bonfire was burning brightly, he took the boy by the arms and threw him onto it. He said, laughing to himself, "Today I will feed on your tender flesh."

The fire hissed and threw a thousand sparks into the air that lit up the fading afternoon with their faint glow. The many-tongued flames licked harmlessly at the body of the child, who stood proudly in the middle of the blaze.

"Oh, moquenquen, now you'll be fried to a crisp," said Agayú, and, taking a branch, he hit him brutally. An omordé was passing. When she saw the child's plight, she ran until she reached the next village and shouted out news of Agayú Solá's crime. The people rose up and began to give their views. Some said: "We should go there and punish Agayú." Others said: "The most sensible thing would be to inform Olofi."

Two women, Oyá and Ochún, agreed to take the news to Olofi after it was decided that his authority must be relied upon to resolve any untoward behavior.

When Olofi was informed of the matter, he said to Oyá, handing her a flash of lightning: "Go and light up the forest. The rest is done." Turning to the other woman, he said: "Bring me the child."

When Agayú Solá saw the flash of lightning approaching, he ran away, terrified, bounding like an ape. He stopped in front of a palm tree and climbed it in a trice. He stayed there, trembling with fear.

Ochún rescued the moquenquen from the flames, and both women returned to Olofi. Olofi said, referring to Changó: "I will make you lord of the fire!"

To Oyá he said: "You are the mistress of lightning!"

Turning to Ochún, he said: "It will be your turn another day. I have handed out a lot of aché today."

And that was that.

Destiny

Changó returned home happy. His wish to see his father had been granted. That was enough for him, despite the harsh reception. In his innocence, he did not know how fathers were supposed to behave toward their children, and therefore his own reception had seemed right and proper. As soon as he arrived, he went to Obatalá and said: "My iyare, I have been with my father."

Obatalá laughed her head off, showing her white teeth. "You won't want to see him again."

"On the contrary, Babá: he gave me a very pleasant day."

"Really? Why didn't you stay with him?"

"I wanted to come and give you the news. Besides, he taught me many things: look." The boy went over to the oven and takes out a burning coal. He passed it over his body and then chewed it, licking his lips as if it were a sweet.

Obatalá said to him: "I see that you can eat fire. Who gave you this gift?"

"My father!"

"Moquenquen, you are lying!"

"I'm telling the truth; my father took me before Olofi and said to him: 'Give my son a gift,' and God replied: 'He will be the lord of fire.'"

13

"What your father has taught you is the gift of lying!"

"Oh, I see that you hate my father."

"Child, you are a lying skirtchaser." Then she seized him and began to smack him hard on the backside until her hands swelled up. The child struggled to free himself, but Obatalá held him between her legs and hit him even more determinedly, saying: "This is so that you never speak to me of your father again."

"Waah, waah, waah," cried Changó.

Obatalá hit him until she fell down exhausted and Changó was swollen and shapeless like a lump of meat.

From then on Changó kept out of Obatalá's way. His spirit was overcome with resentment, and the formerly melancholy child became a boisterous, alarming creature who disturbed the legendary peace of Obatalá's home. He ran from place to place, tirelessly dragging any objects he found along the ground, ringing the ritual handbells. That was some of the time; other times, no sooner had he got out of bed than he began to snoop in all the corners, finding Obatalá's secret objects and throwing them onto the floor with a scornful gesture. His mother punished him severely. When he had taken his punishment he ran over the mountains and turned up at the güemilere. He learned how to dance alongside the drums like the professional dancers, and he gained the affection of those present.

When he arrived they would say: "It is the child that Agayú tried to burn." And the drummers let him beat the drum used at the party with his restless fingers. Changó drank glasses of liquor and in a drunken and euphoric state returned to his habit of grabbing everything.

One day he found an amulet carefully wrapped in soft cotton balls, and, seeing it was very nice, he said: "Do you want to have fun at the güemilere?"

The amulet answered: "As long as you put me back in my place afterward."

They arrived at the party arm-in-arm, like two pals. As soon as the gris-gris heard the music, it jumped up and down three times and danced to the beat. Changó danced with him, following his steps.

Then they said: "Let's have a drink!"

"Well, let's then!"

They drank quickly until they had their fill, and they partied on more wildly, letting the days go by, unmindful of Obatalá and of everyone else. On the sixth day, the güemilere drew to a close with a song to Elegúa, and they went home together completely drunk.

When she saw them, Obatalá said to Changó: "Damn! Didn't you know that Odú-dua must not see daylight?"

"But he's had a good time," answered Changó.

Obatalá, furious, seized him and, holding him up in the air, let him fall rapidly into space, saying: "You are trying to wreck my house; but I'll bury you in the ground first."

Here began the heroic deeds of Changó de Ima.

The Ekuelé
Divining Tray

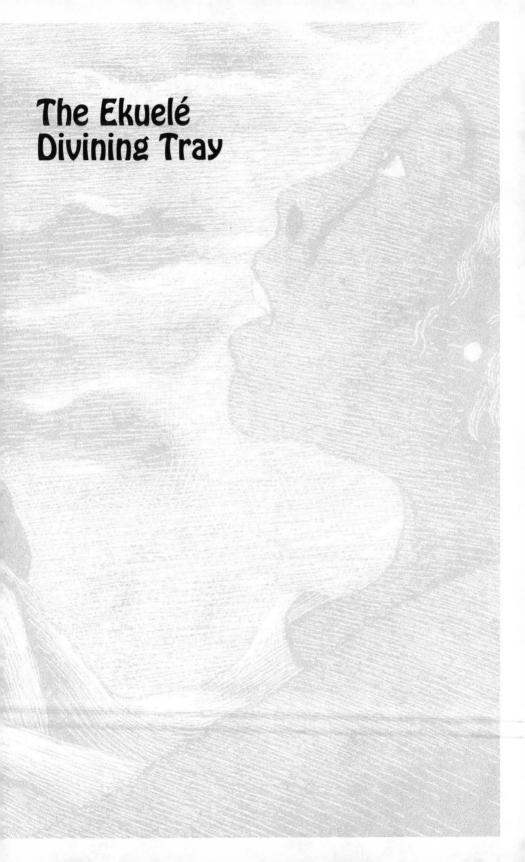

The Revelation

A villager called Yemayá was busy with her household chores when the heavens suddenly clouded over and it began to thunder loudly as if the sky was threatening to shatter into a thousand pieces. The noise of the furious march of the thunder was like the unrestrained gallop of an enormous cavalcade. The advancing clouds cautiously unraveled their curly fleece, moving sluggishly and hiding the last traces of a reddened sun.

Suddenly a flash of lightning cut through space, hurting the eyes of the omordé, who looked up instinctively and was surprised to see a red dot falling rapidly toward her.

Not batting an eyelid, Yemayá opened her skirt out like an net and waited for the incandescent sphere to fall. It shattered in a thick cloud of smoke and threw her to the ground, startling her. After a moment, the woman was even more amazed when she saw before her a child, who was gazing at her and smiling.

"Moquenquen, who are you?" asked the astonished Yemayá.

"I am Changó; my mother has thrown me out of heaven."

"And who is your iyare?"

"Obatalá."

Then Yemayá said happily: "Oh, Changó, you are a gift that

Olofi has deigned to send me. I will raise you with care."

Then she took him to her house. First she gave him a beautiful pair of shoes.

"Nice achó," said the child, putting them on.

Then she gave him clothes. The child threw them away, saying to the woman: "I don't want batá; the best thing you can do is take me to the güemilere."

"I am here to do your bidding, she replied. And, taking him by the hand, she presented him to the drums, and they danced around them until the party drew to a close.

They went back to the house, where no sooner did Changó arrive than he began to scream: "Give me my amalá,[4] miserable woman!"

Yemayá immediately prepared a meal for him, and Changó ate sumptuously. When he was full he demanded: "Now I want to sleep on a mat that is not as dirty as yours."

"Very well, my iyá," answered Yemayá, giving him a richly woven one.

As soon as the boy lay down he fell fast asleep. The omordé slept beside him. But soon afterward Changó opened his eyes and began to kick Yemayá on the behind. "Lazybones, serve your son," he said to her.

Yemayá patiently asked him: "What do you want, my iyá?"

"Find me some drums at once to entertain me," he answered. Yemayá brought him drums decorated with bright red ribbons. Changó took them and spent the whole night playing them and singing:

> Oh, baricosó
> Baricosó,
> Baricosó,

Alardemí oooh!
Alardosó, cabo!
Alardosó, cabo!
Alardemí, oooh!

Roused by the music, Yemayá got up from her seat and began to dance, singing in accompaniment to the child who, seeing her enthusiasm, angrily pushed aside the drums, saying: "My maid, you may not dance, the best thing is for you to take care of me. Go to the forest and bring me some oguedé."

The omordé had to go a long way to indulge him. Taking a sack, she set off and went deep into the forest.

After a while Changó lit a fire and made the ilé go up in flames. Then he went inside and settled down on his mat as if nothing had happened.

From afar, Yemayá saw the sudden blaze and, without having got the bananas, ran to her son's aid. Unable to extinguish the fire, she put her hands on her head and cried: "Olofi, don't let the moquenquen be burned to a cinder."

And as the flames crackle more furiously, Changó appeared from among them and, standing before the woman, said: "I wanted to test you. Where are the oguedé? Coward!"

"How was I to bring them if I thought you were burning?"

"Oh, I can see you're completely useless. I'm leaving," said Changó.

"No, don't do that. Why don't you ask me to do the most difficult thing I can for you, moquenquen," Yemayá said to him humbly.

"Then find me the ekuelé divining tray that Obatalá hides in her ilé."

The woman, even though she knew how difficult her task was,

told the child that she would perform it. She set off on an arduous journey, walking without resting, climbing steep ridges and peaks of sharp rock that covered her hands and feet in wounds, turning them into a misshapen mass. But Yemayá gathered together all her strength and continued her trek. With a huge effort, she reached Obatalá's door and fell down weakly before her, bleeding all over and half dead.

She remained unconscious for a long time. When she came around she was very ashamed when she saw before her Changó, holding the divining tray in his hands and with not a scratch on his body.

He said to her: "See how lazy you are and as slow as an elephant? You took so long to carry out the errand that I decided to come myself. Now I'm leaving."

Yemayá did not even have the heart to answer, nor to plead with him; she was so exhausted that she stayed in Obatalá's doorway, watching Changó fly swiftly over the sharp, prominent peaks of the path of Osan-quiriñán, the only one leading to the house perched on the inaccessible plateau. Then, worn out, she bowed her head and remained there. She stayed like that for a long time until dusk, when Obatalá arrived, wearing all Olofi's attributes. When she saw Yemayá, she rebuked her: "Yalocha, what are you doing in my doorway?"

The woman said to her: "I came to steal the ekuelé divining tray for Changó, but he has beaten me to it, and after he stole it he left me lying here helpless and without the comfort of having him by my side."

"All right, well, now you will remain in my house for forty days and be my servant. That is your punishment for trying to help Changó."

From that day on Obatalá woke Yemayá each morning with the lash and made her perform the most grueling tasks, always reminding her that: "This is so that you won't meddle in my affairs another day!"

On the fortieth day she let her go and put a little necklace into her hands, saying: "This is the ekuelé chain. Find Changó and give it to him in my name. You will be doing him a great favor."

This time she descended without mishap. When she reached her house she found Changó waiting for her with the divining tray on his legs. He demanded that she hand over the chain. As soon as he took it in his hands, he threw it onto the smooth surface of the divining tray and, according to the different positions in which the necklace fell, described to Yemayá the things that had happened to her and gave her rituals for solving her problems.

Yemayá, amazed, said: "Oh, now I understand why I could not raise you: you are the thrower of the ekuelé."

And that was that.

Forgetfulness

When Changó had grown tired of his hurried and itinerant lifestyle, he installed himself peacefully in a house near to where Yemayá lived. He passed the time giving consultations to the villagers with his divining chain. So successful was he at finding out and getting to the bottom of their problems that he was continually consulted by people whose lives depended on the changing positions of his little chain. He acquired the reputation of a great and prestigious diviner and had so much work that he scarcely had time to develop his other faculties.

The day came when, tired of his profession and eager to return to the life of the güemilere, where the drums awaited the touch of his skillful hands, he decided to abandon the ekuelé. He called Orúmbila, a meticulous and contrary old man, and, handing the divining tray and chain over to him, said: "As I'm bored with my job, I have decided to nominate you my replacement."

"Thank you very much," said Orúmbila. "I will honor you as is right and proper."

"But wait," said Changó. "I should give you some advice. You must use your earnings to look after my friend Elegúa."

"How shall I do that?"

"Well, you have to give him a share of the money each time you divine for an aleyo."

"Very well, I will honor your word generously," said Orúmbila. And he began to throw the chain with consummate wisdom and skill. The rumor soon spread that people were praising his exquisite tact and wonderful capacity for helping everyone who turned up with some insoluble problem. However, every night Elegúa arrived at his door to claim his share. But the old man ignored his obligation.

Elegúa complained: "I have come to collect what is mine."

Orúmbila answered: "We'll settle accounts tomorrow."

Elegúa went away without saying a word. The next day he received a similar answer: "It'll be tomorrow; I haven't had time to settle with you today."

Elegúa waited impassively until one day, without saying anything to Orúmbila, he sat down beside his door at the start of the day and waited until those who wanted answers from the ekuelé came rushing to see the diviner. To each one that came he said: "Orúmbila is not seeing anyone today. He is tired." And to others he said: "The old man has taken the day off to visit his wife."

However, at night he turned up as usual to claim his share. "Will you let me have something?" he pleaded.

Orúmbila, completely bankrupt, answered him angrily: "I haven't earned a penny today. Don't bother me!"

And on the days that followed: "You'd better get lost, you lazy dog!"

But Elegúa ignored his insults and went away. Each morning he went back to keep people away. He sat patiently in Orúmbila's doorway, making everyone go away, extremely disillusioned. And gradually their mistrust of the old man grew as word of his unre-

liability began to spread. "Changó did the wrong thing when he handed the ekuelé over to that dreadful old man."

And Elegúa, realizing that Orúmbila could not survive much longer, appeared before him one morning. He found him lying downcast and feeble on his mat. He had lost all his nerve, and his jaw was drooping.

"Oh, Orúmbila, what a state you're in! Have you lost the gift of throwing the ekuelé?"

"No, it's not that; it's that the aleyos are not coming."

"And why don't you consult for yourself?"

"I've done that and I didn't get anything."

"Oh, then you have lost the ability! Call Changó."

When he heard this, Orúmbila recovered what strength he had and said to him uneasily: "What does Changó know about this! I'm the only one who knows how to divine with the ekuelé!"

"Very well," said Elegúa, and he went away. He went back a few days later and found him weak, listless, and unkempt, lying miserably on the floor.

" Orúmbila, shall I call Changó?" he asked slyly.

"Call him," the old man answered in a weak voice.

Changó soon appeared. He entered like a warrior, hitting the ground with his steel sword, wearing a brilliant red jacket. He looked haughtily at the old man. Taking the chain, he toyed with it for a moment, then, giving it a swing, threw it uninterestedly onto the divining tray that was lying on the table covered in powder.

"Cheer up, old man, and tell me what the divining chain has to say," he admonished Orúmbila, who attempted to oblige him.

"I lost the ability a few days ago," Orula confessed.

"Oh, then pay my friend what you owe him, and don't bother

me with such a trifling matter," said Changó, and he went away.

Orúmbila murmured: "The master knows best." And he did his duty by Elegúa.

That is why, before performing any magical work, it is necessary to give an initial share to Elegúa.

And that was that.

Covetousness

Orúmbila continued to throw the ekuelé. He managed to amass a huge fortune. He need only consider that his daily takings amounted to that of a hundred well-paid workers and that, even if he squandered the money and honored his agreement with Elegúa very generously, he had cash enough to rival the most affluent men of his time. But the old man was thrifty and had simple habits. He took greater pleasure in piling up his earnings, foreseeing some turn of fortune beyond the range of his faculties as a diviner.

Elegúa, who visited him regularly to collect his fee, never imagined that the old man, simply by looking at a divining chain and sorting out the daily difficulties of his fellow men, could have amassed so much profit. In order to fund his ambitions, he began to devise a way of going into partnership with Orúmbila and sharing his earnings.

"How shall I approach this miserly old man and suggest he should share his profits?" he said to himself each day, scratching his head. But no honorable idea came to mind. One day, he found an easy solution to his problems. Snapping his fingers exuberantly, he appeared unexpectedly before his benefactor.

"Orúmbila," he said, emptying a hundred coins onto the divining tray, "I have decided to become your partner. From now on we will share the earnings. I will save you the trouble of reducing your savings by giving me part of them, simply because Changó advised it."

Orúmbila replied: "That is a paltry sum. Besides, I had not thought of sharing my earnings, much less with a beggar like you."

"That's all right," replied Elegúa, and he left, disappearing into the forest. After walking aimlessly for a long time, he stopped in the middle of a vast plain. Uttering some inaudible words, he turned himself into three different beings. Beginning thus his magical work, he said to the first Elegúa: "You will remain in the savannah. Your task is to defame Orula."

And he went away, accompanied by the second Elegúa. He stopped in front of the old man's door, saying: "You will station yourself here and send the aleyos to the house across the road." And he installed himself in the said house with the divining tray and chain, and waited.

When the new day dawned, the aleyos took to the road as usual in a long line that led to the diviner's ilé. But when they reached the vast plain they came upon the solitary inhabitant of the savannah. He inquired: "Where are you off to so early in the morning?"

"We are going to consult Orúmbila," they replied.

"Well, then turn back because the old man has stopped being miserly. He is frittering away the money that he steals from you on women at the güemilere."

The aleyos reply: "We don't doubt your word, but we will see for ourselves."

And the convoy continued marching across the plain. When the first ones arrived, the Elegúa in the doorway went to meet them.

He says: "The babalawo has had to go out unexpectedly, and he has advised me to send you to his stand-in at the house across the road."

"Is it true," they ask, "that Orúmbila is squandering the money that we pay him?"

"Oh no! Don't believe the rumors spread by a slanderer," answered the second Elegúa.

And the aleyos, completely trusting, visited in turn the other one who was waiting inside the ilé. He attended them carefully and used the answers of his divining chain to wisely settle their quarrels with false destiny. Each person gladly payed the fee for his visit.

In the days that followed, things happened in the same way; the Elegúa in the doorway always contradicting the one in the savannah. "Don't take any notice of the rumors spread by that jealous person who is trying to hide Orúmbila's merits. He has gone on a long journey: consult his stand-in."

The people eagerly consulted the usurper. With time Orúmbila's reputation gradually declined, and Elegúa's prestige grew. When his magical work had the desired effect, he turned up, prosperous and arrogant, before the real and only thrower of the ekuelé. When he saw him dejected and depressed, he said in an affected manner: "Oh, obiní, what is happening to you?"

Orúmbila weakly answered: "My friend, I have had bad luck since you went away. Do you think Changó could resolve this matter?"

"I don't think so," Elegúa answered coldly.

"Call Changó, and I will do what he tells me to," begged the old man.

"No, I would rather see you die."

"At least give me a plate of food as I've already eaten all my savings."

"Die, proud dog; a man of your class shouldn't beg."

Orúmbila said resignedly, "If I must die then let me die. But who will throw the ekuelé?"

"Who better than I, who have managed to steal your clients," replied Elegúa. And, taking him by the shoulders, he pressed him against the wall, then threw him to the ground and hurled a sack of coins at his feet, saying: "This is so that you can recover. Tomorrow you will throw the ekuelé according to the deal with your new partner."

The old man bowed his head and whispered: "You are extremely shrewd. I accept your proposal." And the deal was closed.

Hereby end the incidents relating to the ekuelé.

Changó

Oyá

Being fond of hazardous exploits and the heroic deeds that enhanced his prestige and added to his fame as a brave and resolute man, Changó de Ima decided to take on Ogún, a renowned warrior and one of the most expert and powerful fighters in the region. Once they began fighting, they battled fiercely again and again. Like the last word, the outcome always hung on the weapons of the two possible victors. The exhausting battles and undecided victories continued for so long that Ogún impatiently suggested to Changó that they settle the affair once and for all in the shade of a ceiba tree, deep in the forest, close to the steep hill where Olofi dwelled. The victor was to appear before him to claim the reward for his efforts in the form of powerful aché.

At dawn on the agreed day, Changó saddled his spirited white colt and mounted it at a leap. Patting its neck, he pulled on the reins until it reared and began to trot jauntily. Exuberant and with a happy heart, he sang the song that recalled his powerful demeanor when faced with his enemy:

A la mofilé
Changó tá molé
A la mofilé
Changó tá molé

But as he was riding across a vast plain the horse was startled by its own shadow and stopped suddenly. Kicking nervously, it refused to move another inch. Changó pulled on the reins impatiently and dug in his spurs, which were as pointed as the tip of a sharp stiletto. Maddened, the animal pulled so hard on the reins that they almost broke and, bucking like a fragile boat battered by a violent whirlwind, it managed to throw its rider. Escaping swiftly, it disappeared into the distance of the unending plain.

Left in this awkward situation, when he had recovered from his fall, the unfortunate warrior gazed for some moments at the cloud of dust raised by the horse's mad gallop. Then, walking with difficulty, he took shelter under a leafy tree. Lost in deep thought, he noticed his spirits suddenly beginning to sink. He was seized by fear, and he began to tremble, his courage leaking away with every shudder of his unsteady and weakened body.

Meanwhile, Ogún waited by the ceiba tree, not suspecting his brave enemy's courage was failing him. Leaning on the handle of his enormous machete, he coldly planned the damage he would inflict on Changó.

Time passed slowly and its endless minutes ate away at Changó, the unfortunate warrior, who lay on the ground like vermin, motionless, having lost his courage. Oyá, the mistress of the cemetery, appeared and found him in this state.

Oyá spoke to him: "Changó, what are you doing in such an unseemly attitude for a warrior?"

"Nothing, omordé, the colt has run away taking my courage on its back. Now I cannot face Ogún."

"I will lend you my braids and my tunic. Thus will your courage return to your body," suggested Oyá.

"I accept. If I return I will repay you with interest."

And Changó, his head adorned with the braids, put the white sackcloth on over his clothing along with his sword and headed for the ceiba tree.

His courage returned to normal and his manly gestures sustained it. As he neared the ceiba tree where his enemy was impatiently waiting, he gathered up his skirt delicately and gracefully and passed in front of it like a refined, slender woman. Ogún, bowing his head, greeted him courteously as if he were Oyá: "Jecua Jey!"

At this, Changó resumed his manly demeanor. Shedding the braids and the dress, with the sword at his waist, he marched towards Olofi. He bowed down before him, placing his sword at his feet, and waited, prostrated on a mat.

Olofi ordered him to rise and said: "You are the lord of lightning."

The warrior unaffectedly accepted his gift and went in search of Oyá to repay the extreme thoughtfulness she had shown him. He said to her: "Oyá, I want to show you my gratitude. How shall I do that?"

"By sharing my bed," replied Oyá.

And they began to live together.

Oyá was jealous of Changó's influence over women and she wanted to have him for her pleasure alone. One day, after she had entertained him for a while with the gift of her slender though mature body, she left him dozing on the mat and quickly went to meet with Death. "Icú," she said, "you must keep watch over my house."

"As long as you feed me well," answered Death.

"Changó is inside; he is a fine morsel for you."

Icú agreed and stationed herself in the door of the ilé. Soon Changó decided to go out. As he reached the door he heard Death's piercing whistle. "Wheee...!"

Frightened, the warrior went back inside, pop-eyed and sweating profusely. His legs were trembling so violently that he could barely stand. He could no longer go out as he would always encounter the cold gaze of Death, swinging her long, coiled tail.

And Oyá satisfied herself, embracing her lover's body that was now free of the marks left by the passionate embrace of her rivals.

Until on one occasion, Ochún, a beautiful, elegant and resolute woman, decided to end the young prisoner's martyrdom. Knowing that Oyá had taken Changó prisoner, using Death as the jailer, in order to fulfil her selfish desires, she decided to corrupt Oyá's morals, outwit her vigilance, and snatch him away. She went to visit her, arming herself with a bottle of liquor, a packet of cascarilla, and a jar of honey. When she reached the door of the ilé, she showed Death the bottle and said: "Icú, shall we have a binge?"

Death agreed and they sat down, amicably embraced. They begin to drink the liquor that Ochún had laced with oñí, seizing an opportunity when her companion was off guard. Icú gulped it down while the omordé held back.

Icú finally got drunk and made an indecent suggestion. "Omordé, let's have sex."

Ochún answered by giving her a kick and throwing her to the ground. Then she went into the ilé and anointed Changó's body with the cascarilla until he was white all over. Taking him by the arm she led him outside.

Seeing Death lying on the ground and emboldened by the effect of the cascarilla, the warrior kicked her three times and followed his companion.

Far away from that place, Ochún hoped the obiní would give
her a night of pleasure to repay her deed, but Changó said warily:
"Omordé, if you see me at the güemilere sometime, I will repay
the debt I have incurred. For now, let me rest in Oyá's arms."

And Ochún resigned herself to waiting.

The End.

The Obeyes

The Obeyes were twins, the children of Ochún's love for Changó. As he did not have time to raise them himself, he abandoned them to life's vagaries. The Obeyes possessed the family traits that immediately revealed their ancestry. One was arrogant and reckless, fond of adventure and with a happy disposition like his father; the other had gentle manners and acted on the whims that constantly came over him. Like his mother, he did things on the spot without stopping to think them over.

These two lads spent their time wandering in the forest and through the villages. Wherever they went they left signs of their good fortune. They were received enthusiastically in the countryside, where men and women farmed the land, and at the güemilere where they surrendered themselves to the call of the drums. When they tired of their nomadic life they stopped off at Yemayá Saramaguá's ilé where they speeded up the pace of the omordé's life. For, despite her affluence she was often dying of boredom in the sleepless, hot, and heavy afternoons.

Changó the drummer often visited Yemayá Saramaguá unannounced. Sometimes she would be with his two sons. He would then lavish stored-up paternal affection on them. He would sit them on his knees and teach them songs that told of his triumphant life and exaggerated the misfortune of others. He astounded them, giving them the wealth of his experience. When it was time to leave they went in opposite directions: Changó to the güemilere, the boys to disappear among the wild flora of the immense forest.

On one occasion, they found Changó perched in a palm tree near the omordé's ilé, consumed with rage. The palm tree was so accustomed to the drummer's excesses that its plumes beat the air gracefully and imperiously, as if slashing the air with a sword. The moquenqueré ran to the ilé to find out the reason for their father's mood. They found a chorus of silent, grieving women, who were weeping about the obiní's behavior. Yemayá Saramaguá was in the midst of them, a cigar stuck in the corner of her mouth, her head hanging, downcast. With her were Naná Bacurú, lying down, a heartbroken Ochún, a downcast Oyá, and Oba, whose eyes were moistened by two shining, glistening tears. The twins burst into the ilé, holding hands, and immediately poured out their happiness. The silence slipped away.

"Oh, the Obeyes," they exclaimed when they saw them come in, and they told them how they had attempted to make Changó happy again, which had not had the desired effect.

"I have recalled our nights of love and danced tirelessly at the foot of the palm tree, but to no avail," said Ochún.

"I took off my clothes, revealing my firm breasts and my perfect belly, but he got even more angry," whispered Oba.

"I served him plenty of food, amalá, his favorite dish, oguedé, ecrú-aró, olé-lé and all the titbits, but he had so little appetite that in his anger he has scarcely moved," said Naná Bacurú.

And finally, coming in through the door, Eleguá said: "I have tried to do without my liquor so as to give it to him but he prefers to remain sober."

"Let's bring him a little happiness," said the Obeyes, and they cheered themselves up by clapping.

The omordés instinctively began to dance and they sang, like a drawn-out lament, the salute to the moquenqueré:

> Oh, lo Obeye
> Oh, lo Obeye
> Oh, lo Obeye
> Odide-ma oooh...!

Ochún stepped forward. Taking them by the hands, she swept them up in the frenzy of the dance. The other omordés danced, moving their hips and gently wiggling their stomachs, heads thrown back. The song burst from their throats.

Eleguá, beating the drums, copied the moves of that remarkable drummer, Changó.

Suddenly opening her arms wide, Ochún cried: "Cabiosile Changó!"

And the chorus responded: "Cabiosileeeee.....!"

Then they went out into the vast forest.

Holding hands, the Obeyes ran in the direction of the palm tree, followed by the women, who were sweating and excited. Their hair flapped heavily in the wind and on the way they cooled down from the fever brought on by the drumming.

At the palm tree the Obeyes sang solo:

> Obidé, odideee eh!
> Odidé, odideee eh!
> Odidé Changooooh!
> Odidé, odide-ma...

The song rose swiftly up the trunk of the tree, which was moved and inclined its plumes. Changó, who was clinging to it with his silver spurs and strapping, hairy arms, abandoned his last shred of arrogance and slowly descended.

Below the women clamored: "Cabiosileeeee!"

Embraced by the Obeyes and bewildered as if he had emerged from a deep stupor, Changó walked along, followed by the women. When he arrived at the ilé he demanded the drums from Eleguá and the güemilere was improvised.

They spent the whole night partying. At daybreak, the Obeyes and Changó said goodbye and went off in opposite directions. Worn out from overwork, his fingers cold and numb as the drums had drawn blood, young Changó decided to rest at Saramaguá's ilé for six days. On his way there he met the Obeyes and they accompanied him.

Six days in the company of the twins livened up the omordé's ilé. The easy nature and happy temperament of the moquenqueré made it seem filled with bright lights and a thousand fountains flowing with joy. Nevertheless, Changó organized his time. In the cool of the morning he trotted through the forest mounted on his white horse, slashing at the thick tree-trunks so as not to lose his skill as a warrior. He would return at midday and demand huge plates of amalá. Then he would rest, lying on his mat while the Obeyes stirred the air over his strong, muscular body with round fans. At sunset, he sang mournful songs filled with nostalgia. By his side, the twins tuned up the drums in the fire and waited for the blood to come flooding into his fingertips. When this happened, sounds like the fluttering of birds escaped from the drums. Sometimes these were cut off abruptly, other times softly drawn out. The Obeyes sang the prayers of the güemilere in plaintive voices.

Yemayá Saramaguá was beside herself with joy. During the day she devoted herself to her housework and at night she joined in their musical evenings. At midnight she would leave them and, taking the gourd that held her savings from its hiding-place, she shone the coins one by one, rubbing them in her hair. Then she took handfuls of them and jingled them happily while Changó imitated the sound, drawing from the drums the notes that evoked Ochún's monetary song:

> Ochún cerequeté
> Mi oguó ooooh…
> Ochún cherequé
> Mi guó…

On other nights the omordé slept with the obiní.

Five days of this happy visit went by. On the sixth, Saramaguá wished to pay a final tribute to the drummer and she improvised a güemilere in the ilé. For this she rustled up the following items: five sheep, fifty full-grown ducks, domestic and tame ardi-die, acucó that sang in the dawning of drowsy mornings, enough ardié-lé—good at judging distances and fond of long journeys—to fill ten pans. From the coconut palms she took all the obí that were lying around. She stole aguardó from the cornfields and lightened the load of the uncomplaining banana trees by stripping their branches of oguedé. Then she began to work diligently.

Changó devoted himself to his daily exercises as normal and the twins stayed to help the omordé, who could barely move amid the enormous amount of food that filled the ilé.

The work was shared out in this manner:

Eleguá decapitated the ducks, using a knife with a gleaming

blade as coolly as if he were testing it by cutting a hair. Then he bled them into a basin that held necklaces with red beads.

The Obeyes sacrificed doves, cocks and hens. They bound them by the legs and, standing firmly on their heads, severed them with a swift traction movement as cleanly as with a knife. They poured the blood into a bowl containing necklaces with blue beads.

Some omordés stoked up the fire and prepared the vegetables. Yemayá Saramaguá saw to the sacrifice of the sheep. Two omordés brought them, feet bound together, mouths tied with strong cord to avoid unnecessary cries and their foreheads marked with a chalk cross. Then they laid them on the floor and Yemayá, crouching over the victim, pulled out a handful of hair and slowly began the execution. A chorus of omordés sang:

> Lube lube yembalá
> Elube Changó oooh,
> Elube amalá eh,
> Elube oguedé eh,
> Elube acucó eh,
> Elube acará eh,
> Elube obi eh.

Yemayá flexed her hands, grasped the knife and slowly began the operation. Raising and lowering the knife until it penetrated the flesh, she drove it in as the chorus cried out. Overcome by deep emotion, excited and panting, she accompanied the song with a drawn-out, halting lament that burst forth fitfully as if coughing up words that rushed into her throat in their haste to come out. The knife went in, making deep grooves in the resisting bones. The omordé's voice died down until it was the distant echo of a plaintive litany:

Lube lube yembalaaaa...
Elube Changó...

Finally the head of the animal was cut off and rolled onto the floor. Seized by an impulse, Yemayá Saramaguá, picked it up and, raising it high, drank the blood that was flowing abundantly. Then she ran deliriously all around the farm holding her booty in her hands, spurred on by the cries of the chorus who shouted wildly: "Cabiosile Changó!"

Some omordés bled the sheep into a large dish while others took hold of Yemayá and carried her in their arms, covering her face with a white handkerchief and quietly muttering some words in her ear, bringing her back to normal.

She performed the same operation five times and just as many they had to murmur the mysterious words in her ears: "By Olofi, by Olodumare, cofiadeno."

The simple food was cooked in the huge bonfire and the Obeyes put them in large dishes and lined them up on the table along with bunches of bananas, coconuts and all the other delicacies.

The hustle and bustle reached its climax. The women ran to and fro, carrying the food. Some were in charge of decorating the ilé and putting things in order, sprinkling sweet-smelling water everywhere.

In the midst of this bustle, Changó returned, worn out by his exercise and with an empty stomach. "I am very hungry," he said and he calmly began to eat the food that was on the table, scarcely bothered by the astonished looks of those present. Dissociating themselves from his behavior, the Obeyes went to Yemayá and complained: "Changó has started already," they said.

The omordé ran to him and tried to stop him but he took no

notice of her and calmly continued eating. Yemayá roundly rebuked him, urging him to wait and eat at the party.

"Omordé, let me eat in peace," replied the youth, barely lifting his head from the plate.

When he had eaten his fill, he stood up and rubbed his hands together in satisfaction. Yemayá looked at him in disgust. Spitting on the ground, she said: "Brave man! That is why you are so afraid of Icú."

When she mentioned Icú, Changó remembered his forced departures from the beds of the omordés and the surrender of his warrior virtues on account of Death, who had besieged him in a comical fashion. Unable to restrain himself, he hit the woman in the face.

"Take that, and see if Icú favors you!"

Yemayá protected her face as best she could, folding her arms, hiding her head and patiently enduring the blows. The other omordés ran away. The güemilere was ruined. The drums lay silent in a corner, and even the Obeyes became sad.

At midnight the obiní ran off with Yemayá's fortune.

When she heard of the disaster, one omordé said that it had all happened because five sheep was too much blood for Changó.

Swift as an arrow, the young celebrant of the güemilere crossed Ogún Arere's domain. Clutching the sweaty neck of his colt, he waded across the fast-flowing river and covered great distances. When the sun was setting like a huge red tambourine following him in his flight, the drummer stopped and settled in the nearby village.

And so Changó's spendthrift life began.

Wearing fine red jackets worked in gold, his fingers covered with rings, he went back to astound the güemilere, drawing con-

vulsive rhythms from the drums. He mocked his rivals with his
frank and sarcastic laugh and once again the women began to
praise him ecstatically: "Cabiosile cabo!"

"Hail to the greatest drummer!"

They filled their pockets with handfuls of the coins he squandered as if he were reaching into a bottomless sack. He changed
horses whenever he noticed the slightest irregularity in their trot,
the harness had to be of the finest quality and the spurs had to
prick like sharp arrows. If not, the youth raged and beat his ser-
vants. However, these tantrums made further holes in his bottomless bag which, caught up in his giddy life, he had not foreseen.

He loved women without bragging. He was so good in bed that
the omordés would wait a long time hoping that he would grant
them a few moments of pleasure. When the time came, it was
enough that, embracing his body, they could pour out the reserves
of love accumulated in the antechamber of the caresses that the
youth's promiscuity had delayed.

With men he was generous and a good confidant. He filled with
coins the pockets of those who came to seek help from his sack,
with no further obligation. To those who sought advice on love, he
offered the fruits of his experience. And for the unfortunate and
fainthearted, he predicted happy events if they emulated certain
gestures and behavior. His arrogance subdued and restrained the
untrustworthy until they became harmless creatures.

As he was reckless, he brought the wild course of the güemilere
to a standstill on many nights, exchanging the drums for the ekuelé
necklace. He threw it on the sand and predicted inevitable deaths
and inestimable fortunes, giving and taking away hope from people's hearts. Then he would randomly erase these predictions,
returning to his drums and playing them at breakneck speed, beat-

ing them hard. The unlucky bemoaned their adversity while those favored by fortune emptied their pockets of happiness deep in the heart of the drums, where the officiant recalled the bold fights of warriors and the remarkable deeds of men. Amid the confusion, men and women would cry out urgently as they kept having to pay their solemn respects to the important visitors who arrived.

"Jecua Jey!"

"Jecua Babá jecua!"

"Yeyeo!"

Changó was swept along by his life of ease and grandeur until one morning when adversity must call, greeting him with its icy hands.

The gourd where he kept the coins had become shriveled and depleted. In his pockets remained only traces of his constant withdrawals the night before. The youth realized that his senseless life had come to an end, but he was not disheartened.

He waited for nightfall and, like a brave-hearted gambler, headed for the güemilere to turn over the final cards of his winning streak. But luck escaped him on a turn in the road. Men turned their backs on him and, for the first time, the omordés noticed that a man without property was unattractive.

Without his white horse and having lost his self-possession, Changó returned to Yemayá Saramaguá's ilé. Alone and dispirited, he walked along the roads where he had sunk the hooves of his spirited colt on triumphant runs and raised huge clouds of dust. The harsh rain lashed his gaunt and sunken face and the pounding of the wind carried away his strength, pushing him to and fro like a puppet. Slowly but surely the weather wore away his last crimson jacket until it was completely ragged.

Disheartened, his hands in an attitude of entreaty, the arrogant youth reached the door of Saramaguá's ilé on a dull afternoon. Eleguá casually dismissed him. "Be off, thief!"

The wretched one accepted the insult uncomplainingly. He drowned his sorrows by drinking from the last bottle of liquor that fate had placed in his hands to make it easier to bear the shame or at least serve as a reminder of his former grandeur. But on this occasion, Eleguá snatched it from him and emptied it down his throat in one gulp. Once more Changó swallowed the humiliation. Coolly and calmly he watched the man who was so cruelly driving home his misfortune.

Eleguá's gaze became fierce, his body swayed and he fell flat on his back in front of the door he was guarding. Changó seized the opportunity and a flash of the boldness that had been crushed by the weight of his poverty passed through his mind. Not losing a moment, he silently entered the ilé and took with him the Obeyes, who were sleeping at the foot of Yemayá's mat. Dragging them to a remote place, he lifted them onto his knees as before and said: "I am depressed, I need your help to gain Saramaguá's confidence."

"We must help you with everything," replied the Obeyes.

"Then when you go back to the ilé sing this song," he retorted, breaking into song:

> Yemayá-n coroná
> Yemayá-n coroná
> Camaguá erío
> Changó lorisa
> Yemayá-n coroná
> Yemayá-n coroná

The moquenqueré sang along with him in soft voices until they

learned the music, They announced that they could now sing it to
the omordé, and promising to let him know what would happen,
they returned to the ilé.

The following morning, standing proudly before Yemayá, the
children began to sing, holding hands and dancing rhythmically.
The omordé listened to them, frowning and nodding her head
wisely but then she suddenly stopped them, saying: "You are wast-
ing your time. Changó will not come back to this house!"

She began to hit them and told them not to go back to see the
drummer. But once they had recovered from the punishment, the
Obeyes decided to disobey Yemayá's order. Changó had only to
announce his arrival at midnight, singing it to the savannah, for
them to escape straight away and go to his side.

This was the song:

> Zacuta mío,
> Agua cessi,
> Egdo midee.
> Dale yaluma!
> Agua cessi,
> Egdó migdeee...!

"Yemayá beat us," said the Obeyes, clinging to his legs.

Confronted with Yemayá's rejection, Changó decided to undo
the knot joining together so tightly that pair who, in the days of
their happy childhood used to wander through the forests and villages spreading good fortune. And he spoke to them thus: "One of
you will run away with me when Yemayá is oribule."

And thus it happened. At midnight, one of the twins, certain the
omordé was sound asleep, slipped from the mat and, crawling

along the floor, left the ilé. Braving the darkness, he ran towards
the ceiba where the shadowy figure of Changó was moving impatiently. Pulling him along by the hand, he walked with huge, echo-
ing steps towards the undergrowth. Crouched down and squashed
together, they spent what remained of the night. In the morning,
leaving the moquenquen in his hiding-place, Changó went into the
bushes in search of nourishment. When afternoon came, he cautiously headed for Saramaguá's ilé. He arrived at the moment
when the drums and handbells of the old yibonas were sounding.
A general meeting had been called when the moquenquen's loss
was noticed. Concealed among the crowd of villagers, he heard
Yemayá's plaintive voice asking for everyone's help in finding the
other half of the Obeyes, who had vanished mysteriously and
whose disappearance had plunged her into deep sorrow. A large
and strapping woman, her ample flesh was growing slack. She
staggered, barely able to stand on her plump legs. When she had
made her speech, the crowd, angered and moved, separated into
groups that disappeared along the thousand pathways of the forest
in search of the missing moquenquen. Yemayá, bathed in tears,
and the proud and arrogant Changó were left alone.

"Saramaguá, your sorrow is mine, I will give you reliable news
of the moquenquen."

"No, no...Go and look for your son!" the omordé exclaimed
and collapsed at his feet.

With astounding cruelty, the youth kicked her unconscious
body. He retraced his steps, heading for the güemileres that were
silent as the whole village was wandering through the forest in
search of the twin. Later he went to keep the Obeye company
in his hiding-place concealed by the tall grass in a secret corner of
the wood.

That night the villagers rested after their fruitless search. The following morning, accompanied by drums and bells, they rushed into the wood once more, determined to get the moquenquen back. Changó seized the opportunity to meet with Yemayá on his own. He said: "I have taken the long way: I climbed the high peaks; I have gone into the darkest caves and I have searched the whole earth from the top of a tall palm tree without managing to find the moquenquen. Could Icú have taken him?"

"Oh no! The moquenquen is alive. Bring him to me," Yemayá's spirit was broken.

"Well, Icú has swallowed him and now I will take the the moquenquen who is left. Without the other one there are no Obeyes," said Changó coldly. Entering the ilé he took the child in his arms and went away.

Yemayá ran after him, shrieking loudly. As quickly as he could, the drummer went deep into the wood until he ran into the searchers. When they saw him with the twin, they exclaimed:

"Changó has found him!"

"How happy Yemayá will be!"

But he was followed by the omordé, who was seized with hysterical laughter. Her eyes had dried and her weeping had turned into laughter. Behind those who followed Changó, she broke off her incessant constant laughter to implore: "Stop him, he is going to kill him!"

Changó, followed by the crowd of people, retorted: "Don't take any notice of her, she is so happy that she has lost her mind."

The moquenquen smiled brightly, amused at his father's cunning.

The drummer led the whole village through the undergrowth. Still laughing, Yemayá was caught up in the crowd of men and women and moved forward until she was at the front. Letting out a sharp whistle, Changó made the other moquenquen appear out of the grass and embrace the omorde who stopped laughing. They were reunited in the presence of the villagers, who were touched.

Here ends the legend of the Obeyes.

The End.

# Incest

In the glorious days of his lavish and opulent life, young Changó would rest lying on his mat and pass in this way the hot hours that dull the mind and confuse the spirit. His mother Yemayá often kept him company, curling up tenderly at his side until they both fell asleep. But one day it happened that the mother was attracted by her son. Moving closer to him, she gently brushed her body against his. This made her tremble slightly. Her flesh gradually weakened until, seized by a sleepy somnolent sensation, she hugged the youth more tightly. To calm the desire that suddenly came over her, she began to caress him gently and very subtly. Her overflowing sexuality proved stronger than the restrained caress, so that, quivering and with a faraway look, she embraced her son passionately while she was trembling and throbbing. The attempt woke the youth and, recognizing his mother, he cried out, horrified: "Saramaguá!"

Yemayá replied: "My iyá, I want you…"

Using his arms as a lever, Changó pushed her away, flinging her across the room. He quickly took his purple jacket and his trousers, got dressed and rushed out of the ilé.

The youth ran off his distress and confusion in the savannah. He

stopped in front of the tall palm tree that welcomed him in moments of difficulty. He climbed it and attempted to overcome his anger there. But Yemayá, who had recovered from the humiliation caused by her body, pursued him, running wildly. Her ample breasts rang out in an unending peal the lust of the omordé who allowed herself to be carried away by her powerful sex drive.

High up, Changó tried to recover from his anger. He held on to the bending trunk that swayed its plumes in the wind. There below him stood Yemayá Saramaguá, crying out to him with her arms outstretched: "Obiní, finish satisfying me!"

From high Changó answered: "Omordé, find an animal like yourself!"

Sighing deeply, Yemayá lost patience and threw herself to the ground, digging her sharp nails into the earth. She stretched out her body wildly and rubbed her private parts on the hard, improvised bed, calling out longingly to the youth who was trying to overcome his anger at the top of the palm tree. "Obiní, I will give you unheard-of pleasure."

And the youth, convinced that Yemayá was shaming herself more by this impropriety than the embarrassment already caused by her desire for his body, climbed down and embraced her.

Their bodies rolled over in confused movements. Going against nature, they possessed each other for a long time.

Since then the mother has loved her son.

The End.

Oba

Oba was a girl of firm and solid proportions, whose figure flowed in a slender line that crowded into the rounded forms below her waist, and whose thighs were so slim they appeared to glide down towards her extremely narrow feet, hinting at the slight roundness of her knees. On the nights when people were woken by the frenzied sound of the drums, Oba liked to have handbells rung insistently in her ears until her body rolled to the floor, trembling and shaking. Seized by a profound ecstasy, she stretched herself like a cat in the sultry noonday heat.

Oba was a yalocha of ancient lineage. She was destined to marry a man who was a warrior by profession, a high-ranking occupation that indicated the distinguished status of those who practised it. And so it was that, on one occasion, Changó de Ima appeared, the victor of bloody combats and a handsome and seductive youth. Taking her slender hand and confident of his high rank, he said: "Oba, I take you as my wife."

And they began their married life.

The warrior Changó was a good lover and also an unrepentant gourmet who enjoyed good food. His favorite dish was amalá, which he had served to him in large quantities. For this reason, he told his wife that she should take as much care over his cuisine as of her own virtue. Oba promised and did not let him down.

Soon after they were married, Changó had to go to war. He adorned his chest with warriorlike purple and a yellow belt from which hung his enormous solid steel sword. Mounting his thoroughbred white colt, he set off in search of the laurels of victory. Oba followed behind him with two sacks of provisions on her back, humbly going on foot, which made her husband's authority appear greater.

Changó de Ima was going to challenge the warrior Ogún over an aché that Olofi had offered him.

The first encounter took place at a crossroads where the two warriors found themselves by chance. Changó drew his sword and hurled himself at his opponent, who was approaching with his chest bared, showing the scars that fame had given him. He was armed with a double-edged machete, so huge that it had to be handled with both hands. But Ogún dodged the blow. Taking two steps back and steadying himself on his strong legs, he offered to fight him. They viciously clanked steel and the forest echoed. Changó made his horse rear up and swooped down on Ogún once more. He dodged the assault and attacks, ripping his enemy's purple shirt with a single thrust. He sliced the air three times without meeting his target. Then Ogún spun his machete round and, moving ten paces from his opponent, quickly rushed at him, stabbing to the right and left until he broke Changó's sword in two. It fell to the ground preceded by a shower of sparks.

Thus disarmed, Changó de Ima did not lose his head. Digging his golden spurs into his horse he made it rear up on two legs, using it to block his outwitted enemy, who was already showing signs of fatigue.

However, the fight continued until they both left the battlefield, completely exhausted and with the victory undecided.

Changó returned to his wife and impatiently demanded food. "Oba, I've had a difficult day today, give me plenty to eat."

His wife liberally obliged him. But when Changó had finished he asked: "Wife, I am not full, bring me more amalá."

Oba went and brought him more.

Changó was satisfied and he lay down to sleep until the following day. In the morning he got up and, taking a brand new sword, went out once more to test his weapon.

The arduous and fierce battle commenced, but this time Changó had to return home with his thigh pierced by Warrior Ogún's sharp machete. He vented all his anger on his unfortunate wife. "Oba, wife of the devil," he said, "bring me three plates of amalá!"

Resigned and humble, his wife did her duty without looking up.

Changó treated his wound and on the third day he went off once again to thrash Ogún the Warrior. But once again luck did not favor him and he returned with the wounded colt. Entering the ilé, he shouted irritably at his wife: "Slut! Fix me five plates of amalá!"

Silently Oba did her duty.

The terrible fight between the two most famous opponents of the warrior epics continued for ten days. Capricious victory sometimes settled on Ogún's head and other times on Changó de Ima. During these ten days Oba's provisions were gradually depleted. When that happened, the woman lay on the ground and bewailed her difficult situation, for she had gone through the whole forest without finding the mutton that was the main ingredient of the amalá. But the desire to meet her obligations was stronger in Oba than the defeatist act of weeping. Thinking that her husband must arrive at any minute, she took a knife, cut off both her ears, and added them to the flour which bubbled and popped as it boiled. Then the woman went into the bedroom, suddenly convinced that she was no longer beautiful. She wept with her head buried in her thighs.

Soon afterwards her husband came in, ostentatiously cleaning his blood-spattered sword. His manner suggested that he has come off best in the contest.

"Wife, bring me the amalá and come and share in your victorious husband's laurels."

But Oba did not answer.

Changó repeated the call: "Oba, come into my presence."

Once more silence was the reply. The husband changed his tone: "Idle woman, come and attend to your husband!"

The husband became impatient and went into the bedroom, finding her lying on the floor hiding her head in both hands. Changó pulled her furiously by the hair: "Oba...!"

When he saw her head without its ears, he stepped back several paces, filled with horror, and finally said: "Oh wife, I do not love you without ears!"

His victory turned to disappointment, Changó vanished into the forest.

Oba, who on hot nights had little bells rung repeatedly in her ears to then fall down, trembling, to the sound of the drums that recounted the adventures of ruthless men and haughty women, went into the forest when she realized how futile her sacrifice had been. She began to run along the paths that were strewn with flowers, stricken with heartrending grief, leaving behind her clusters of trees that listened, perplexed, to her anguished cry: "I am Oba, she who is no longer beautiful!"

And she burst out crying, shedding copious tears that soaked her body, which was undamaged by the tragedy of her mutilated face. She continued on her journey, going sometimes across the shimmering plain, sometimes along steep and arduous paths that cut through the forest, always crying pathetically: "I am the woman without ears; now I can no longer have a husband!"

Lost in the depths of the jungle, her sobs were so mournful that they filled the radiance of the noonday wood with sadness. Her tears were so copious that they filled the empty basins of a small stream: Oba turned into a river.

And no one has ever heard again of the omordé with the slender figure and the rounded buttocks. All that remains is the gentle murmur of the stream where lies hidden the legend of the woman who sacrificed her beauty on the altar of duty.

The End.

Ochún

Echú and the Pumpkin

Ochún had a vegetable garden sown with such lovely big pumpkins that there was scarcely room to walk in it comfortably. With Ochún's care and skill, the pumpkins grew fine and abundant. She put a great deal of effort into cultivating them and gave them the best part of her free time. Moreover, she treated them all equally, and the pumpkins were happy to have such a good, hardworking mistress.

On one occasion, a pumpkin began to grow and became so unusually beautiful that it stood out from all the rest. Ochún, seeing it so fine, was captivated by it and began to treat it differently from the others. She paid them less attention. Realizing that their new neighbor had captured the affection of their mistress, they began to be filled with jealousy and agreed to plot against the upstart.

One night they stealthily approached the pumpkin who enjoyed such advantages and began to hit her mercilessly. They said: "Intruder; you have stolen Ochún's affection away from us. We will kill you. Ochún will have no choice but to love us. Take that and that." And they beat her violently.

"Ouch, ouch," cried the defenseless pumpkin. The pumpkin

managed to escape. She ran away and swiftly reached Ochún's house. She hammered desperately on the door.

"What is that banging?" asked Orúmbila, Ochún's husband.

"Let's see who it is," said his wife, and she went to open the door.

The pumpkin said, "Let me take refuge in your house, for they want to kill me."

"Oh, you have escaped from the garden? Come in."

The pumpkin told her mistress of the others' envy and jealously. She begged her to allow her to live in her house as she feared the violence of the others would kill her. It was not fair since she was the finest of them all. The most natural thing should be that she would live so as to excel and be able to enjoy the good things of life.

Ochún said, "Sleep peacefully; they won't bother you anymore."

The pumpkin settled down in the bed between the husband and wife. But halfway through the night Orúmbila woke up and said to the pumpkin, "Sleep on the floor, because I'm not comfortable."

The pumpkin said nothing and settled down under the bed. In the morning she got up and said to Ochún, "Your husband doesn't like me."

"Don't worry; I will help you with everything," said her mistress. And then she headed for her bedroom, took a sharp, shiny sickle, and set out for the pumpkin garden. She cut away all the reeds, stabbing at them violently while saying: "Take that for mistreating my favorite. Take that for incurring my anger."

When Ochún finished, she returned home. And the pumpkin said to her, "Thank you for honoring me in this way. Now I will be the only one who deserves your attention."

"From now on I will be your protector," said Ochún.

And the pumpkin said, "I will pay you back with interest."

At that time, Orúmbila was earning a lot of money throwing the Ifá. When he finished his work, he put the coins in a sack and placed it in a secret hiding place. Then he went out. The pumpkin watched him do this and began to covet Orumbila's money. Thus, each afternoon when the old man had gone out, she went to the hiding place and stole a handful of coins, which she concealed in her bosom. The pumpkin grew extremely fat.

One day, Ochún, wishing to caress her, clasped her passionately to her chest. "Pumpkin, how fat you are!"

And the pumpkin made a jingling noise.

"What's that noise?" asked Ochún.

The pumpkin replied, "I'm robbing Orúmbila for you."

"You are clever, pumpkin. From now on you will be my moneybox." And the pumpkin was pleased to have her mistress as an accomplice.

Another day Echú turned up at the house and said, "I'm going to move in here until I see this couple ruined."

When the pumpkin heard this, she retorted, "Don't think that things will go so well for you."

"Who are you?" asked Echú.

"Me? Ochún's moneybox."

Echú began to hit her, and the pumpkin said, "I will give you a bottle of liquor if you stop hitting me."

"Done deal," said Echú.

The pumpkin brought him a bottle and said, "I will give you all the liquor you want if you don't get in Orúmbila's way. Treat the old man mercilessly."

"Very well."

From then on, Echú sprinkled the four corners of Orúmbila's

house with a concoction of his invention, and the old man's business began to decline. Alarmed, Orúmbila consulted Ifá, but when he threw the chain it fell forming intricate patterns that the wise diviner could not decipher. Orúmbila resigned himself to bad luck. The day came when he did not even earn enough to eat.

The pumpkin said to Ochún, "Now the old man doesn't even earn enough to be able to steal a coin from him."

"The poor man! Bad luck, he's having a spell of bad luck. Shall we help him?"

"Don't count on me."

"Miser!" said Ochún angrily.

Echú and the pumpkin were discussing Orúmbila's fate. The pumpkin asked, "How far are you going to take the poor old man?"

"As far as I please."

"You should leave; you've already done him enough harm."

"Don't poke your nose into other people's affairs!"

"Hee, hee, hee," laughed the pumpkin, sure that Echú would not leave Orúmbila alone until he had destroyed him.

And she gave him more liquor. She was lavish with her generosity. One time Echú drank too much and fell down in the middle of the road. He did not realize that Ochún was approaching. Seeing him lying on the ground, Ochún prodded him gently with her foot, saying: "What are you doing here?"

Elegúa did not answer, and she prodded him more forcefully. "What are you doing here?"

Elegúa slowly opened his eyes and answered: "Ask the pumpkin."

The pumpkin, when questioned, said: "I had no idea he was around, I haven't seen him hereabouts."

Ochún said: "You have been plotting with Echú." She slapped her twice and left.

When Orúmbila returned at nightfall with a wild expression on his face and sunken cheeks, like a ghost, he fell into a seat and said: "I'm dying!"

Ochún asked him: "Haven't you eaten?"

Orúmbila did not answer. Ochún thought that Icú had taken him away. Desperately she picked up a weapon and went to take her revenge on the pumpkin. The pumpkin ran and shouted: "You have fattened me up with Orúmbila's money and now you want to kill me!"

Ochún finally caught her and with a single stab of the knife, cut her in two. All the gold spilled out at Orúmbila's feet.

The old man, seeing the gold, cried: "Yalorde, you were the mistress of the ogúo!"

Orúmbila's Parrots

Old Orúmbila, the Ifá diviner, was respected for his prestige and wisdom. As the result of a special favor from Olofi, he married Ochún, a woman of warrior stock. She was a beautiful girl who men found irresistibly attractive. She tempted them using the subtle power of oñí, the charm she used to captivate Olofi himself.

For the convenience of his profession, Orúmbila installed his wife in a mansion situated on a vast plain. It was easily accessible to the aleyos who came to discuss their misfortunes and to receive the embó that would improve their luck. The aleyos came from afar in a long caravan that traversed the most arduous routes. Orúmbila's prestige was such that everyone made sacrifices in order to hear him speak comforting words and to live in accordance with that which destiny had ordained.

Orúmbila made plenty of money. He had enough to keep the greedy Ochún in sumptuous style. By nature she was fickle and given to deceit. They lived happily. They had a nice home, a good income, and enjoyable pastimes, but one thing worried Orúmbila. Every day his sex drive was decreasing, and Ochún, who was young and proud of her sexuality, demanded from him what he could not give her. "Let's go to bed," Ochún would demand. And he obliged her with his flagging virility. "What a man Olofi has given me," his wife complained, and her eyes filled with tears. Orúmbila understood that Ochún was a young woman. One day she would look to a younger man to provide her with what he could only offer her in a hazy memory of his younger days. He expected that the time would come when his spouse would spend in the arms of another the reserves of pleasure that he had caused her to accumulate.

That day came. Deep in the forest, his domain from one end to the other, lived the warrior Ogún Arere, the uncouth king of metalworkers. He intimidated his neighbors simply by tramping heavily through the land over which he reigned. Ogún Arere would only enjoy a woman once. He would use them violently and then push them away cruelly. But Ogún did not dare to be so impetuous with Ochún, as one day she had given him delicious pleasure.

Ogún said to her: "Woman, visit me always, I will give you expensive presents."

Ochún's various love affairs made her forget the incident, and they did not meet again. Her marital disaster with Orúmbila refreshed Ochún's memory, and she thought about the warrior and his powerful exuberance and wild energy when enjoying a woman.

One morning, Ochún, elegantly attired with five scarves tied round her waist, seven necklaces jingling at her neck, and smeared all over with honey, took the road to the forest to look for the metalworking king. At the foot of a leafy ceiba tree she found him lying on the grass in a deep slumber. Ochún began to undress swiftly. Naked, her body smeared and gleaming as it reflected the sun's rays, she began to dance while she sang a song of desire:

O-lo oñí oooh
Yeyé oñí oh.
Oñí abeeeee!

Ogún suddenly woke up. When he saw her he exclaimed: "Yalordé!" He tried to embrace her, but Ochún slipped nimbly away and danced dizzily until she fells exhausted into Ogún's arms.

"Ochún, you haven't changed."

"We will see each other every day."

Filled with foreboding, Orúmbila divined for himself. The chain gave him some indication of the betrayal. Orúmbila waited cautiously.

One afternoon when Ochún returned, she heard birds fluttering inside her house. She advanced swiftly and silently and saw that the house was full of parrots. Holding her breath, she listened to the cacophonous chatter of the parrots. The parrots were saying: "When will the adulteress return?"

"She'll be here sometime. We will tell him everything."

Ochún did not act foolishly. She went into the living room, pretending to be very happy. "Oh, how kind Orúmbila is. He's filled my house with parrots," she said.

The parrots watched her. "My parrots, would you like to eat?"

"Yes."

"Yes."

Ochún gave them otí mixed with oñí and said to them softly: "Omoyú lepe-lepe."

On that occasion not much happened. When Orúmbila arrived, the parrots said: "Ochún did not go out. Ochún is more virtuous than you think."

Orúmbila was not reassured by the parrots' declaration. He was aware of his wife's cunning. Orúmbila waited.

Ochún said to him: "How happy I am with my parrots! They amuse me in your absence."

"That is why I brought them."

But Orúmbila waited.

One day the master of the house arrived home and noticed that the parrots were immobile, in a deep sleep. He made a lot of noise to wake them up, but to no avail. The parrots kept on sleeping. Nothing could waken them. In a moment of absent-mindedness Ochún had added too much otí, more than she should, to the birdseed. The man said nothing; he remained silent.

His wife said: "What's wrong with my little parrots; why are they so fast asleep?"

"Because they've had too much to eat."

Orúmbila did not say anything more. At night they went to bed. Orúmbila could not do anything, nor could Ochún. They were worried.

The following morning, Orúmbila said: "Wife, go to the forest and bring me oguedé. I have a craving for them."

Ochún went without saying anything. As soon as her husband was sure that he wouldn't be surprised by his wife, he went over to the parrots and daubed their beaks with epó, saying: "Now you will have no choice but to tell the truth."

Orúmbila devoted himself to his work. He divined for the aleyos with his usual impassiveness. When Ochún came back, the old man took the bananas and began to peel them calmly. As he ate he said: "Don't give the parrots anything to eat. I have already done so. You'd better see to the housework."

"Very well."

When Orúmbila went off, Ochún very discreetly gave the parrots the birdseed mixed with oñí or otí, muttering the words: "Omoyú lepe-lepe." And she went to meet the warrior Ogún-Arere, whom she told of Orúmbila's suspicions. The metalworking king responded by piling gold into her hands. Ochún set off for her large house, expecting that everything would be resolved to her advantage because she had a lot of faith in the power of her oñí.

Orúmbila was calmly waiting for her. As soon as she entered the house, the parrots begin to chatter with a deafening racket. They were saying:

"The adulteress has arrived."

"She has come from seeing Ogún Arere."

"Orúmbila, your wife is cheating on you!"

"Kill her!"

Ochún began to hit them furiously, crying: "Traitors, toadies!"

Parrots always tell the truth.

The Sacrifice

They say that when Ochún was in her prime she used to enjoy herself at güemilere whenever she chose, boldly confronting the gaze of the lads who looked admiringly at her swaying body. Her waist was narrower than that of a woman of more noble birth. Her fingers tapered like the blade of a sharp dagger. But even with expert wooing, no man managed to have the pleasure of lightly brushing against the skirt of that omordé, more cunning than sensible. Sometimes on hot nights Ochún would allow herself to be pursued by handsome, well-built lads whom she brought into her ilé and granted brief nights of pleasure.

The omordé's waist was so slim that it could be encircled by a child's tiny arms. Her hips were so narrow that, when her arms were folded, she could pass through a slender hoop from head to toe.

One day she turned up at the güemilere presided over by Changó, the handsome drummer, whose fame was recounted in tales that passed from village to village. Ochún asked permission to speak a few admiring words to the most dexterous of the drummers. She went over to the drums and, bowing her head, ceremoniously said to him: "Emí, you are the greatest of the drummers. Please deign to visit me."

Changó interrogated her: "Who should I ask for?"

"You should ask for Yalorde, your humble servant."

"Oh, Yalorde?" said Changó, and he thought for a few seconds. Suddenly he replied: "You are not worthy of my attention," and he continued to play his drums.

From that moment on, Ochún, wearing the most outrageous clothes, did not miss a single day of the güemilere that was presided over by the indolent youth who dared to humiliate her in front of all her admirers. On one occasion she took off her tunic and danced right beside the drums. Her whole body was smeared with oñí that dripped from her narrow fingers and fell to the ground like drops of gold. Everyone watched fascinated as the nimblest dancer at the güemilere moved restlessly.

Changó calmly dripped some oñí onto his face and said gravely: "Cofiadeno, omordé."

Ochún ran away with her head bowed and two tears filling her deep black eyes.

The following day Ochún went back to Changó. "Please deign to share the bed of the most desired woman ever born," she said.

"Ochún, leave me alone," he answered and went on presiding over the celebrations.

Despite this, Ochún persevered. On one occasion, choosing the moment when the drummer was resting from the exhaustion of the night, she slid silently onto his mat and, using delicate flattery, prepared the youth who could not resist her extremely skillful caresses.

When they finished, Changó said: "Omordé, you're not good at handling men." And he turned his back on her.

This partial victory of Ochún broke the ice, and they continued to see each other on the nights that favor lovemaking under the full moon, which revealed the accessible paths of the forest, or they coupled on the damp grass of the open spaces, because, in spite of everything, Changó did not give Ochún an inch.

He humiliated her frequently: "Ochún, you are not worthy of my bed; you don't know how to make love to men."

"You are clumsy and as sluggish as an elephant. You stay stuck to me like a slug at the moment when any prudent woman moves away."

Ochún bore this stoically like someone betting on a hunch. But the moment arrived when fortune turned its back on Changó, and he became less popular at the güemilere. He regarded his downfall impassively. His pride made him abandon his job rather than suffer the ridicule of passing unnoticed in the place of his greatest successes, and he settled in an ilé far from the raucous sound of the drums.

Ochún went there and comforted him. She gave up all her possessions and took with her just one dress that she fastidiously washed every day in a bend in the river. Ochún took her tunic to the river so often that, once white, it became yellow and washed out. From then on, Changó began to feel love for Yalorde.

Ogún Arere's Trap

Old babalochas tell of how Ogún Arere, who ruled over the immense forest, selfishly wanted to keep for himself all the profits from the bountiful harvests and incalculable riches the forest hid in its interior. Thus no one was allowed to traverse its paths. So as to avoid the bother of chasing after them, he concealed traps in the dry grass along the pathways. Many men of an adventurous nature had interred their foolhardiness in attempting to defy the will of the mighty farmer.

Each morning Ogún Arere inspected all his traps. Bare-chested and with a machete slung through his belt, he walked with heavy, swaggering steps, using a long stick to push aside the dry grass. When he saw the deep holes, his bloodthirsty nature was satisfied to see how many men lay there packed together, struggling against death with no hope of any reward and not having had a chance to take their leave of life bravely.

This practice continued for many years. It ensured that the farmer's territory remained undisturbed. He felt confident of his authority when he saw that the traps contained old and fossilized bones.

However, one day Olofi, whose authority could not be questioned, ordered Orúmbila, his most trusted servant, to go into the forest to collect some of Ogún Arere's obí. Orúmbila trembled from head to toe. But he had no alternative but to obey. As he was skinny, he thought he would be able to slip safely past the hidden traps. The following morning he set off with a sack of provisions over his shoulder to trust his life to fate. He became hopelessly lost and began shouting in the forest. But his cries echoed feebly around its cavernous depths and could not be heard outside the forest. Old Orúmbila understood that his agony had begun. He lowered his head onto his chest and was resigned to die. The earth began to eat away his flesh, which was already wasted. Little by little only the sorry remains of a human were left; flies were buzzing around it, and worms lay in wait.

All that remained of Orúmbila was the spirit of a man when, one morning, three cheerful and talkative women were going through the field picking flowers along the pathways. They stepped unwittingly on Ogún Arere's graveyards. The traps, many now laid bare, were lined with loose bones. The women walked lightly over the grassy surface, revealing the long line of graves with their harvest of skulls and entwined bones.

One of the women was Obatalá, a gentle, serene girl; the second was Yemayá, plump and lissome; and the third was Ochún, nimble, frivolous, and alluring. She went in front. Either to show that she was unmoved by the grisly spectacle or because she knew of no other way to subdue her emotions than with a song, she began to sing softly, waving her hands in the air:

> Yeyeo oñí oh . . .
> oñí abell
> securé a la yumó! . . .

Oñí abé.
Securé a la idó! . . .
Oñí abé.
Securé ibucolé! . . .
Oñí abeee . . .

Meanwhile the others stifled cries of horror, and their bodies trembled when they saw the new traps. The three women were startled to hear a loud snore coming from one of the holes. It was Orúmbila's death rattle. At that moment the three women leaned over and saw him, tall, thin, and bent, with his nails clawing the earth as if he was grasping at his last hope.

"My abure, it's Orúmbila!" Yemayá said to her sister Ochún.

"Let's save him!" said Obatalá.

Ochún, untying the five handkerchiefs she normally wore at her belt, made a strong cord and a lasso, and between the three of them they lifted out the old man, who was half dead.

They carried him before Olofi. He received him without much surprise and did not seem to be very interested in Orúmbila's mishap. He said to Ochún: "Go and deal with Ogún Arere."

To Yemayá he said: "Liven him up!" And she made him drink a bottle of liquor.

At Olofi's request, Obatalá also took him in her arms. Murmuring some words in his ear, she calmed and revived him, for she is the mistress of human understanding.

Halfway through the afternoon, Ochún entered the forest and ran from one end to the other shouting and attempting to attract the farmer's attention. When he heard her, Ogún Arere irritably pulled out his machete and went in pursuit of her. But when he found her he changed his mind and asked her in a perfectly normal voice: "Omordé, what are you looking for?"

Ochún, who had greeted him lying naked on the ground, let him know her intentions with a salacious gesture, and she replied: "Nothing, I have come to enjoy myself with you." And they had sexual intercourse.

Taking out a bottle of liquor that she had concealed, the woman then said: "Drink this liquor."

Ogún Arere, stunned by the ruthlessness of what had just taken place, obediently tipped up the bottle and became completely drunk.

Ochún quickly ran to his hiding place, stole all his money, and ran away.

Ogún Arere, filled with shame, found he no longer needed to take precautions and allowed free access to his domain.

Deception

Olofi granted a simple obiní called Ogún Arere, who was sturdy and cantankerous, the honor of being the supreme lord of the immense tracts of the forest. Thus he was beyond reach of all social relations and only had contact with his fellow men when he wished to test his strength and impose his authority. He guarded with an uncommon zeal the area between his domain and the neighboring villages. No living creature could attempt to cross it without risking being cruelly affronted.

Although Ogún Arere was able to conquer women and give them maximum satisfaction, he also turned his unseemly temper on them. He embraced them powerfully and vigorously and then, after possessing them, would beat them violently. No woman could boast of having visited him more than once. Nevertheless, on dark nights the omordés slipped through the forest and lay in wait for him on the grass, where the farmer would take them brutally and savagely.

On account of the legends about the rather ungallant habits of this powerful farmer, on the night of a moon that seemed to throw torrents of light into the dark forest, Yemayá Saramaguá, a lively and vigorous girl uninitiated in the mysteries of love, entered the

wood. She went down paths with hazardous intersections breaking
the silence all the while with a song that lamented the sadness of
her body in the first flower of womanhood:

> Acolona oooh!
> Aeee!
> Dale yaluma oh!
> Dale ayaba mío,
> Oñí abeee!
> Si Yemayá ta secú secú.
> Si Yemayá ta cuelé cuelé
> Epooooo!
> Ucineba oooh!
> Aeeee!

Ogún Arere, armed with a machete of gigantic proportions, half
naked and displaying a mop of rough, curly hair, was wandering
about when the echo of her voice made him stop suddenly. He
headed in the direction of the bold young woman's song.

Yemayá Saramaguá saw him coming. Her whole body trembled
slightly, and she cried in a trembling voice: "Hey Aguanillí!"

He settled down to wait for her in a turn of the path. The girl
went along the track, and Ogún Arere threw himself on her. He
raped her in jerky spasms until Yemayá, trembling all over, rubbed
her exhausted body against the man's strong muscles. He pushed
her away, but the girl was inflamed with desire. She came back
and embraced him, murmuring: "Aguanillí, keep on filling me up.
I'm not satisfied!"

Ogún Arere disengaged himself. Holding her by her delicate
waist, he threw her to the ground. But the maiden, whose desire

was not diminished by physical pain, stood up swiftly and went stubbornly toward the farmer. He took a step back and, brandishing his machete and chopping the air, threatened her angrily: "I will have to kill you, insatiable bitch!"

The girl gave up in the face of such opposition. Filled with terror, she started running to the edge of the forest and went to her ilé. Yemayá was desolate and had a heavy heart. She still carried the marks of Ogún Arere's powerful virility on her thighs. She ran to look for her experienced sister, Ochún. In between sobs she told of her misfortune and asked her to use her cunning to punish the farmer's brazen deed. "My abure," she said, "a man has humiliated me. After he possessed me, Ogún Arere left without satisfying my desire."

"Don't worry, I will bring him to you at night so that you may have your pleasure."

Armed with a plate brimming with oñí, Ochún went along the long path leading to the forest that was crossed by little streams. She went as far as the place where the mighty river flows, heaving warily like a gigantic boa. Ochún, who is called Yalorde in güemilere songs, passed through the dense jungle, clearing a path with her arms and filling the forest with her song:

> Securé a la yumó oh!
> Securé a la idó oh
> Yeyé oooh
> Oñí abeee!
> Securé a la yumó oh,
> Securé a la idó oh,
> Yeyé oñí oooh!

When they met, Ogún Arere, fiercely eager, tried to seize her
arms, but the woman swiftly evaded him and placed her plate of
honey on the ground to await his next move. The farmer, who was
looking daggers at her, was overcome with rage, and he repeated
the action. The girl slipped away easily and danced before him
freely, defying his attempts to embrace her. The farmer clumsily
clutched at.air, attempting to grasp the güemilere dancer's beautiful body.

She stole away, swaying like a stalk of maize in the wind. In the
frenzy of the dance, Ochún took one end of her skirt and spun
quickly until it came off. She held it in her hands like a sail with
the wind in it and let Ogún Arere see her curvaceous, sweaty, glistening body. The farmer stayed there, enraptured by that outrageous woman. Pausing in her dance, she took the plate of oñí and
poured it over her body that now cried out for moments of love.

The farmer seized the moment and got on top of her, holding
her by the waist. Ochún moved her hips restlessly like a trapped
fish. Once more she mocked him, laughing loudly enough to fill
the entire wood. Ogún Arere, panting, his hands smeared with the
charm, was clumsy and bewildered. The omordé, seeing she had
won, cunningly entered the deep forest. She went ahead, singing
her song:

> Yeyé oñi oh.
> Oñí abee!

Aguanillí followed her as meekly as a lamb. When they reached
the edge of the forest, she lay down and artfully revealed her
ample bosom and aroused body.

Ogún Arere took her noisily and as greedily as a miser.

"Omordé, you have not left me entirely satisfied," he said, half exhausted.

Ochún replied: "Let's do it indoors," and she dragged him to Yemayá Saramaguá's ilé, where she was lying on her mat, waiting patiently.

It was a dark night, and the farmer didn't notice the other woman. He settled down with Ochún in the bed. She got up from his arms and left him with her sister, who silently replaced her all night long. "Will you come back, obiní?" Yemayá asked the next morning.

Realizing he had been tricked, Ogún Arere hit her furiously and went away.

Here ends the story in which Ochún, the most beautiful girl at the güemilere, violated the strict principles of the formidable Ogún Arere.

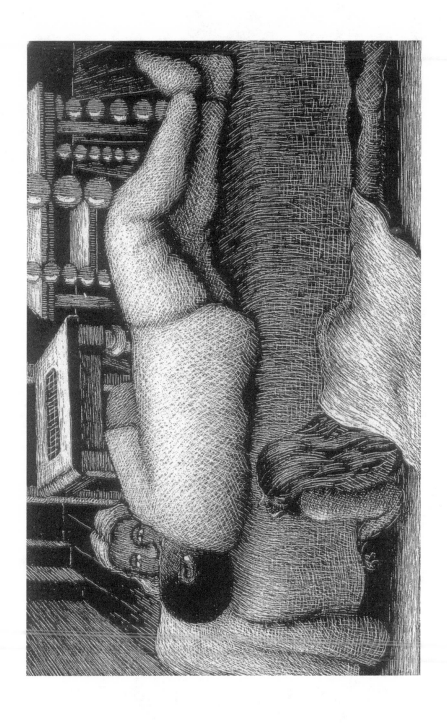

Yemayá

Orisaoco

They tell how, anxious to find a farmhand who would be able to take charge of sowing her yams, while at the same time revealing absolutely nothing about the procedure to be followed in order to obtain the prized crop, Obatalá asked young Orisaoco to help her. His chastity was the topic of conversation everywhere. On account of this virtue he was a hard worker and there was no danger of the secret being revealed because of some woman meddling in his life.

Wishing to discover how well the youth could keep the secret that she would, after all, have to reveal to him so he could carry out his duties, and knowing that some men were weak when faced with women's desires, Obatalá called him aside. Acting like a loose woman, she showed him the parts of her body decency requires should remain hidden, leading him to understand that her desires were those that would be a puzzle easily deciphered by any bright youth. But Orisaoco, ignoring her seductive pose, turned his back on her and went away.

Pleased with the result of her experiment, Obatalá called him the following day and entrusted him with her delicate charge. "Orisaoco, I am going to give you a job that will increase your prestige and wealth but the price is complete silence about the secret that I will confide to you.

And the youth agreed and promised to be discreet.

With his hard-working nature and the shrewd and clever way he concealed his labor, Orisaoco sowed Obatalá's field from one end to the other. On fine nights, a traveler passing by would not fail to hear the murmuring of the talkative yams. They would poke their heads to the surface of those mounds of earth that resembled long rows of graves and served as their shelter and recount their troubles in order to use the faculty that Olofi had granted them of being able to talk like people.

Obatalá was always commenting in a complimentary way about her farmer's abilities. This reached the ears of Yemayá Saramaguá, a woman who enjoyed her patronage. Obatalá did not wish to grant Yemayá's obvious wish that she favor her adoptive son, Changó, the fruit of one of Obatalá's indiscretions, with the gift of the drums. Yemayá thought that by corrupting Orisaoco's morals she would set a trap for her benefactress. By snatching the secret from Orisaoco, if all else failed, she could return it to Obatalá in exchange for her granting Changó the gift of becoming master of the drums.

In the meantime, at the first sounds of morning, young Orisaoco went to his plantations, hoe across his shoulder and walking with a jaunty step. Using his tool, he dug into the earth, piled it up and slipped in the seeds he carried. Yemayá was shrewdly spying on him. She carefully followed all his movements, but he dropped the yam sprouts into the earth so deftly that the omordé remained baffled and did not discover his method. This made her decide to simply approach Orisaoco and obtain the secret using her caresses.

One morning, she turned up unexpectedly, wearing a sheer tunic that outlined her lovely, ample breasts which were quivering in their flimsy confines and hinting slightly at escape. Bending her body backwards, she offered herself like a ripe fruit, lush and fleshy. Orisaoco discouraged her with his naive incomprehension of what this meant and he carried on with his job. Yemayá bit her lips and yielded to the youth's cold manner. But the next day, managing to catch him at break time, she gently caressed him, examining the youth's thin flanks inch by inch until the last remains of his chastity were in her hand. When he sensed himself mounted by the woman, Orisaoco felt as if he were entering a new life. And he could not imagine his long period of inactivity.

Yemayá knew how to push her advantage home.

The man in Orisaoco was awakened by her impatient compliments. On their sleepless nights, the yams raised their smooth heads to the surface and discussed the deflowering of the farmer, who, eager to make up for the lost days of his passion as quickly as possible, was allowing himself to be possessed by Yemayá Saramaguá in those planted fields, entrusted to him because of his chastity.

He was so stunned by his recent transformation that during his working hours, stooping tiredly, he placed the seed clumsily in those mounds that were gradually becoming uneven as the omordé who was the mistress of the youth's movements went with him, spilling fistfuls of aguardó into the furrows he made.

Time passed. When the moment came to harvest the fruit, one dawn that saw night retreating with the curly, diaphanous clouds opening their curtains to a still-sleepy sun, Orisaoco, hoe on his shoulder and followed by the omordé, went to dig up the fruit of his labors. But to his amazement, he saw that all his work had been undone. Astonished, he allowed suspicions about Yemayá to pass through his mind. He confronted her: "Omordé, you have ruined me. How can I face Obatalá?"

Yemayá replied coldly: "You have seriously insulted me by mistrusting me so I am leaving you. Sort yourself out with your mistress as best you can!"

And she went away.

Orisaoco, deeply depressed, went into the forest, bearing on his back the excessively high price that the omordé had placed on the discovery of his manhood. And nothing more was ever heard of the chaste youth, who used to go jauntily, hoe on his shoulder, to cultivate gentle Obatalá's fields.

In Changó's fields the yams told of poor suitor Orisaoco's misfortune, while in her domain Obatalá contemplated her ruin with stoic indifference, realising that Yemayá was the reason her farmer had disappeared into the forest shedding impotent tears. She did not reproach her for her behavior but waited for events to reveal how she should be punished. Emboldened, and at that difficult time, Yemayá demanded from her the drums for Changó. She got a negative answer. She then urged Changó to give Obatalá a present from his sown fields.

Changó loaded his horse with yams and went through the forest singing about his triumphal presentation to the mistress of the drums:

> Ilé mi, ilé masó
> Sacuata ilé,
> Indiá acucó...

When he reached her, he threw the yams at her feet. He declared he was very glad to serve her at such a difficult time and offered her his humble assistance.

Obatalá answered: "You have done me a great favor; take the

drums and enjoy yourself at the güemilere for six days, then return them to me!"

And she handed him the drums. When the time was up, Yemayá said to Changó: "Give me the drums to take to their mistress who will keep them for a few minutes, for they shall be yours for ever."

Changó agreed and gave them to her. They were immediately returned to Obatalá but when she took them in her hands, she threw them to the ground with a gesture of disgust and said: "I don't want them; take them away!"

It so happened that Yemayá had smeared them with orí and Obatalá was so fastidious that, ignoring the stratagems they had set in place to counter Yemayá's scheme, she allowed herself to be defeated by that omordé's shrewdness.

Thus Changó became the master of the drums.

The End.

Ogún Arere

Cunning

Ogún Arere, the lord of iron and a warrior by profession, appeared before his sworn enemy, Changó de Ima. He suggested calling a truce in one of the long drawn-out battles that they frequently fought, sometimes for completely trivial reasons, sometimes to win the honors Olofi bestowed on the victor. But these proud and majestic warriors mainly fought to indulge their warlike natures.

On this occasion Ogún Arere said: "Changó, I am tired of fighting; let's rest until the next moon."

"Very well, I accept," replied Changó, using his sharp, shining machete to cut the slender stem of a bush with an affected abandon.

Ogún Arere, making an effort to be polite, bowed his heroic head and said insincerely: "Your good sense greatly pleases me. Had it not been so, your death would soon have been a tangible fact."

"I see that you are a braggart," replied Changó calmly, cutting a hair with his shining machete.

"Well, Changó, I have not come looking for a fight. Instead we should take advantage of this truce by passing the time somehow."

"What game do you suggest?"

"Well, let's go to the beach and we'll see who's best at collecting shells."

"Oh, I'll beat you! I'm a hundred times quicker than you."

"Then let's bet something on it. The winner will take the loser's fortune. Do you accept?"

"With the greatest of pleasure."

"Then we'll meet tomorrow on the shore."

Ogún Arere left him and set off for the house of Oyá, the keeper of the cemetery. He proposed the following: "I want you to rent me Icú early tomorrow morning."

"That depends on whether you pay me a decent amount."

Ogún Arere handed her six bags of gold, and the deal was closed. The following morning Icú would simply turn up on the beach.

The wager began, and the rivals industriously gathered the shells that were scattered on the sand. From time to time they watched each other suspiciously out of the corner of their eyes. They put the shells in the bags that hung from their arms, moving in opposite directions, bent over, engrossed in their not altogether honorable task.

Changó gathered the shells unhurriedly, every so often humming softly and tauntingly:

> Ogún Arere,
> Meyi meyi mellizo
> Ogún Arereeee.

And just when he was at his most tuneful, Icú came and kicked him on the backside. Changó turned angrily and bumps into Death, who was serene and enigmatic.

"Hee, hee, hee," laughed Death.

Changó dropped his sack, performed three cartwheels, and ran off faster than a buck to hide.

That night he got a visit from Ogún Arere, who provocatively threw two sacks full of shells at his feet. Changó, the loser, bowed his head in shame and handed over all his wealth.

Ochosi de Mata

Ochosi de Mata

Olofi, the father of heaven and earth, called his assistant, Orúm-bila, and spoke to him thus: "Orúmbila, it would please me if you fetch me a quail."

"A quail?" replied Orúmbila, astonished. "No human being has ever managed to trap one."

"I command you to find me a quail."

"It is difficult, Olofi; set me another task."

"Fetch me the quail from within the world's boundaries."

"Very well, you shall have it," replied Orúmbila, realizing that any attempt to dissuade his master would be futile.

The next morning, Orúmbila went into the forest with his quiver full of arrows and his gleaming bow. He began walking along a long path that went deep into the dense forest. Then he crossed mountains that were arduous to climb. A thousand times he confronted the quail, a thousand times he shot his bow in vain, and as many times saw his attempt fail. He went along every path and used up all his arrows, and the quail mocked his skill as a hunter.

Orúmbila became discouraged. When the sun began to go down and night was falling, dark and full of a thousand omens, Orúm-bila, tired and downcast, took the path that led to the villages.

In the villages the people noticed the traveler with his empty quiver. He was covered in mud, more discouraged than exhausted by his prolonged effort, and had a detached expression. Orúmbila looked at everyone worriedly, trying to find in each the person who would be able to get him out of his predicament. From time to time he stopped in front of groups of people and said: "Olofi wants a quail. Whoever gets him one will receive powerful aché."

Some of them, noticing his defeated look, laughed in his face and went away. Others replied: "You are asking a lot. We can't fulfil your ambitions."

Orúmbila began to despair more and more. He went from village to village, and his footsteps raised clouds of dust, as if Orúmbila wished to punish the earth. He reached places where brave men were able to perform the boldest feats, and he came into contact with real hunters who had made an art out of their trade. The only answer he got was:

"We can't."

"We can't."

Orúmbila no longer had any idea of time. Night gave way to day and day to night. Once, twice, three times. And the traveler, covered in mud, unhappy and frustrated, heard only these discouraging words from people's lips:

"Your endeavor is ridiculous."

"Why don't you earn the aché for yourself?"

Deciding to go back and await from Olofi the punishment he deserved for his failure, Orúmbila took a long, narrow path where the echo of the forest's sounds faded. He walked slowly and wearily. He went deep into the wood and heard the sound of distant drumming that resonated through his entire body. He headed quickly toward the place it was coming from. As he got closer, his

body vibrated and his feet pulled him along as he were gliding effortlessly to the beat of that music. His spirits lifted. Orúmbila became a new man. Close by, he heard the song very clearly:

> Ochosi aqui-l-odara
> A la mata dé.
> Ochosi de Mata,
> Oqué oqué
> Yambere iloraaaaaa
> Y de mataaaaa!
> Oqué oqué!

He reached the place where the drums were reverberating. It was the güemilere with drums decked with red ribbons to greet Changó, blue ones to pay tribute to Yemayá, yellow to greet Ochún, and white for Obatalá. The great party of the saints. Everyone wore festive white sackcloth and beaded necklaces that glinted in the sunlight. Bit by bit, the drums lifted the spirits of those present. They got faster and faster, playing a thousand notes. Everyone fell to the ground gyrating voluptuously and then rose up beating the air with their hips and singing:

> Yambere iloraaaaa
> A la mata deeee.

Orúmbila approached the drums. He surrendered to the insistent music, and, twitching his body like a snake, he gave himself up to the party.

The most striking people there were a woman, a real woman who swayed and danced tirelessly and as delicately as a palm tree,

waving her arms majestically in the air. It was Ochún, queen of the
güemilere. And also a stout, manly lad who danced with the girl,
feigning an amorous devotion that was dispersed with the sounding of each note. This was Ochosi de Mata.

When the party had quieted down a little, Orúmbila asked:
"What is the reason for such merriment?"

"We are honoring Ochosi de Mata, the greatest hunter," they
replied.

Then Orúmbila said: "I am Orúmbila, Olofi's assistant. I would
like to speak to him."

Those present bowed down until their foreheads touched the
ground, making moforibale, and they hastened to call Ochosi.

He appeared.

"Ochosi," said Orúmbila, "Olofi has deigned to appoint you the
hunter of the quail."

"An honor that I deserve, you shall have it tomorrow."

"Good."

The güemilere went on until the sun showed its glowing face.
In the late morning, Ochosi went to the countryside and caught the
quail. He went back to his house and left it in the care of his mother. And he informed Orúmbila, who asked him: "Have you performed your errand?"

"Of course."

They both headed for Ochosi's house. When they arrived, he
made Orúmbila wait in the doorway while he went inside. A few
moments later he came back with a distraught expression and
trembling with rage: "They have stolen it!" he exclaimed, starting
to walk to and fro, shouting: "My iyare, you know what happened
to the quail!"

"I don't know, nor do I care," she replied.

"You have deceived me," Orúmbila said calmly.

"No," cried Ochosi, desperately.

"Ochosi," Orúmbila said in the same tone, "I will give you another chance. If you bring it to me you will receive aché from Olofi; if not, you will pay dearly."

"I will bring it to you, Orúmbila!"

"Good, I will be waiting."

They parted company.

Ochosi, raging and taking powerful strides, broke through the forest in search of the quail. Eventually he found it and caught it once more. "This time you will definitely not trick me," he said, and put it in his bag.

At once he looked for Orúmbila. "I have it now; let's take it to Olofi," he said.

They followed a mountainous path and, heading toward the top of the hill where Olofi's white dwelling lay, climbed until they disappeared from view. They arrived and stopped in the doorway. Orúmbila knocked three times and waited. Olofi appeared with majesty and pomp, and they both prostrated themselves on the floor.

"Here is the quail, father," said Orúmbila humbly.

Olofi took it in his hands and stroked it gently while watching Ochosi de Mata out of the corner of his eye. Suddenly he adopted a serious pose and, stretching out his right arm, said: "Ochosi de Mata, I name you king of the hunters!"

"Thank you; you have given me a rank that I deserve," said Ochosi, prostrating himself. Then he got up nimbly and, taking his bow, fired an arrow at random. And he said: "Olofi, may the arrow stick in the heart of the person who stole the quail."

"So be it," they answered.

Ochosi de Mata went down to earth. When he entered his home he gave a cry of horror and ran out, hands on his head, saying: "Olofi, you have killed my mother. My iyare! It was you!"

His mother was stretched out with the arrow in her chest.

Ochosi de Mata stopped in front of a tree and let himself fall down heavily. He was deeply distressed. He lowered his head and threw the quiver of arrows to the ground. He gave himself up to weeping. He shed floods of tears. As he was a man of determination, he resolved not to use the power Olofi had granted him if it would discredit it.

One day when Olofi had ordered him not to go into the forest to hunt, Ochosi went into the woods. He began to shoot arrows to the right and to the left. Suddenly he saw a fine specimen approaching and took better aim. But as he fired, the animal turned into Odú-dua. The hunter was so afraid that he remained there petrified, holding out his bow in the action of shooting. Thus Ochosi de Mata became a legend.

Here it ends.

Orúmbila

# Orúmbila's Moquenquen

There was a time when there was no more delicious morsel for Olofi than the steaming, grilled flesh of a lad or a nubile and well-bred maiden, carefully selected from the most distinguished families. On one occasion, his faithful servant Orúmbila was on his way to the village where they were waiting to hand over the specimen intended for his master's lunch when he met a fine-looking boy wandering round the outskirts. To save himself a long walk, he caught him and presented him to Olofi on a shining dish. When Olofi tasted the first mouthful, he liked its fine taste and he asked: "Orúmbila, what kind of meat is this?"

"It's moquenquen meat," he said.

"Well, it's delicious. From now on give it to me instead of the other."

Pleased with the happy outcome of his laziness, the old man went down to the villages. Gathering everyone together, he explained Olofi's changed tastes. He exaggeratedly praised his refined palate and urged everyone present to bear in mind the gift of the moquenquen, which he would deliver to his destination.

Those assembled said in unison: "Of course; we will be honored to procreate in order to sustain Olofi."

Thus, in the days that followed, Orúmbila had only to say: "I have come for Olofi's food," and they would hand over the boy, saying: "Take the family's finest offspring."

But this new departure so whetted Olofi's appetite that when he finished one he would say: "Orúmbila, this morsel hasn't filled me up; bring me another."

The old man obliged him by bringing him another boy. And he must have eaten up to five at one sitting. This annoyed the villagers, whose wives found themselves in the humiliating predicament of bearing children simply to feed the appetite of the unscrupulous Olofi. And they gathered together to discuss how to prevent their children meeting such a terrible fate.

The omordés said: "We should not have to give birth in order that lazybones may eat"

And the obiní said: "We should hide them in the forest." And that is what happened.

On the following day, Orúmbila arrived at a door, and they forestalled him. saying: "If you have come for the moquenquen then you will have to go away empty-handed."

"But I have come for another reason."

Then the omordé started to cry and said: "Orúmbila, the moquenquen was taken by Icú last night."

Orúmbila left. The next day he went to another ilé and got the same answer: "Death has taken the moquenquen away."

And thus, on the days that followed, the old man was greeted with the same answer while Olofi fasted. Until, on the fourth day, no longer able to contain his hunger, he summoned his assistant and said to him angrily: "My guts are sticking to my backbone. You must bring me food right away!"

Realizing that he could not answer back, Orúmbila went out

and, after walking to and fro in search of a solution, he headed for Eleguá's ilé. "I need you to get me a moquenquen," he said.

"You will have to pay me dearly."

"I will give you a bottle of liquor."

"Done deal," answered Eleguá. And he went into the forest and surprised the crowd of children who were playing happily in the bushes, having completely forgotten their former destiny. They had gotten fatter and become stronger and more lively in that peaceful, safe place.

Eleguá, pretending to be good, mixed with them, but the moquenqueré greeted him warily: "What are you doing here, old dodderer?"

"Nothing; I have come to teach you an amusing game."

The boys, seeing him so good-natured and vague, begin to trust him, and they said innocently: "Well, let's see this game."

"Let's make a bet on who is the best runner in the savannah," answered Eleguá. "I will race against one of you."

"Come on, decrepit old man, you can't even crawl," answered the boys, laughing in his face.

Eleguá, without turning a hair, insisted, and one of them finally agreed to test his stamina against him. At the signal they started to run. Halfway the old man pretended to be lame; he fell down, and his opponent overtook him.

The other boys went up to him and said teasingly: "See how you've worn yourself out?" And they started laughing at him again.

Eleguá stood up with difficulty and he asked them to give him another chance, claiming that he tripped over an unseen obstacle. His opponent agreed. But this time he ran swiftly, leaving the moquenquen behind.

The others who were anxiously watching the spectacle were

amazed. The old man surprised them by running as swiftly as a gazelle, and the boy, out of breath, lost speed, little by little. Then they complained: "You have won unfairly. The moquenquen was tired," they all cried.

The old man replied: "Very well, all of you race against me then."

"We'll do that," said the protesters. And, lining up alongside him, they started running.

Eleguá cunningly sometimes let them get in front and sometimes ran alongside them, spurring them on as he gradually gained their confidence and led them imperceptibly down a path that ended in an enclosure. At this point he ran faster than they. The moquenqueré, eager to beat him, ran blindly until their little bodies crashed into the barriers and they fell down in a confused heap. Then the old man hurried to block the entrance, saying: "Now I will hand you all over to Orúmbila." And he ran to find him.

When Orúmbila saw the moquenqueré squirming in fear and confusion, he handed the liquor to Eleguá and said: "I see that you are crafty. I will give you all the liquor you want."

"We'll discuss that another time, for now, take what is your due."

In the enclosure, the boys wept and moaned, letting out piercing cries that sometimes turned into a single deafening and pitiful shriek. Only one boy remained calm and instead of complaining, walking to and fro quietly, as if all this were quite normal. Suddenly he began to sing softly and melodiously:

> Orúmbila talardé
> Babá moforibale
> Orúmbila talardé
> Babá moforibaleee

The person referred to in the song was startled. Quickly opening the fence, he took the boy in his arms and asked him: "Who taught you to sing like that?"

"My iyare."

"What is her name?" Orúmbila asked.

The boy replied: "I don't know who my father is, nor my mother. I was born with the song and I sing it because it is nice."

Orúmbila said nothing. He took him before Olofi and urged him to cease his cannibalistic yearnings, saying: "This moquenquen is my son whom Ochún abandoned. I looked for him everywhere without finding him. Now by chance your excesses have placed him in my hands. This is why I want all the moquenqueré to be free from being devoured by your cravings."

Olofi answered him coldly: "Since you have obliged me to fast, I will eat this boy. From now on, I will seek other forms of sustenance. Your wish is granted."

And Orúmbila served him his son on a colorful dish.

Orúmbila and Icú

A very thin and unhealthy-looking omordé, visibly disturbed by some great affliction, arrived one day at Orúmbila's door. Her face was soaked in tears, and she was sighing deeply. Falling to her knees, unable to contain her weeping, she spoke these faltering words: "Orúmbila, Icú is prowling around my house. Don't let him take my good, tender boy away."

Seeing her so downcast, Orúmbila said: "Go into the forest and gather four baskets of okra. I will wait for you at your house."

The old man immediately set out for the ilé. He goes into the bedroom and leans over the bed where the boy, making every effort to fight off death, was lying. With a small piece of chalk he marked a cross on his forehead that burned with fever. Then he waited for the woman to come back. Spreading the okra on the ground, he covered it over until it looked like a green carpet. He ordered the omordé to leave and, positioning himself in a corner, awaited Icú's arrival.

Death entered in a martial fashion. But no sooner had she taken a few steps than she lost her balance and began to totter, slipping on the green floor. Her footsteps exploded the okra pods with a dry crackling sound. Finding herself in a position quite unseemly for

130

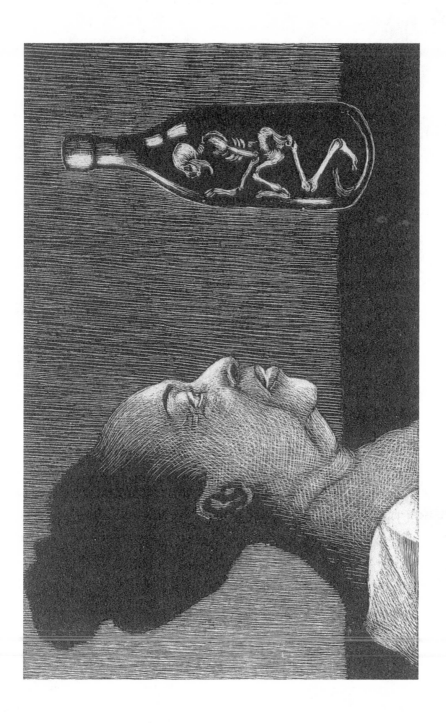

someone of her rank, she made feeble efforts to grasp invisible supports in the darkness until, thrown completely off her center of gravity, she fell to the ground noisily, like a sack of pebbles. She let out a cry of indignation: "Wheee!"

Orúmbila immediately came out of his hiding place and, cracking a poplar switch, hit her vigorously. Faced with this punishment, Icú managed to stand up, hopping to and fro and swelling to enormous proportions. But the old man continued hitting her with his whip until he reduced her to a tiny dot.

Icú had no choice but to look for a way out. Jumping up, she climbed into an empty bottle that was lying in a corner of the house. Orúmbila put a cork on the hiding place and chastised her more vigorously, saying: "Icú, now you are in my power!"

She replied: "Release me from this humiliation, and I will readily accept your terms."

The old man took her to the moquenquen, whose closed eyelids avoided the prisoner's deadly gaze. Showing her the cross, he said: "Do you see that sign? Well, that means that whoever has it is under my care, and therefore you must respect him. Do you agree to my terms?"

"I will gladly accept them," said Icú.

And Orúmbila let her go.

The moquenquen was completely cured. Since then, the superstition remains that on her jaunts, Death tends to lodge in bottles. That is why it is dangerous to leave them unstoppered.

Here I have said it all.

Songs or Prayers of the Güemilere

It begins with *Eleguá*.
He is invoked with the following words:

> Echubí, Echú, laroyo, Echú baragó,
> Echú de baranqueño. Con el permiso
> De Olofi, de Olodumare.

The person who is invoking him then stands before the saint. He pours water on the floor three times, twists his body slightly, leaning backwards, and stamps his left foot on the ground three times. The first song or prayer, which is obligatory at all ceremonies, is this one:

> Echú, oh, oh, oh.
> Eleguá a la eeeeh
> Eleguá moforibale,
> Eleguá a la eeeeh
> Echú, oh, oh, oh...

Another:
> Echú baragó
> Echú baragó
> Echú baragó
> Moforibale Eleguá coroná
> Ichonchón abé,
> Ichonchón abé.

Odara coronilé yó.
Odara coronilé yó.

And the last one:
Agó Eleguá buquenquen
Agó moyuba buquenquen
Let us go to the feet of my Eleguá.
Agó Eleguá buquenquen
Agó Eleguá buquenquen.
Let us go to the feet of my Eleguá

One may then begin invoking the other saints.

Ogún Arere.
He is invoked by saying: Jey Aguanillí jey!
Moforibale is performed, that is, he is greeted by standing
before him, raising the arms with clenched fists and making a
hitting gesture.

Prayers or songs:

First:
Aguanillí ooooh
Ogún Arere
Ogún fomalé
Ogún agué aribó
Orí bam bam

Another:
Ogún Arere

  Sellecilé aguanillí.
  Bam bam...
  Ogún Arere
  Sellecilé aguanillí
  Bam bam!
  Ogún Areré
  Sellecilé aguanillí
  Bam bam!

Another:
  Ogún de Areré oh,
  Irebombo locuá.
  Aguanillí oooooh!
  Irebombo locuá eeeh!
  Ogún arona.
  Irebombo locúa eeeh!
  Ace, ace...Ogún dé.
  Ogún de Mata quilonché.

And finally:

They say: Ogún Aguanillí free me from Icú.
  Quita aro,
  Sara yeyé bacuró
  Sara yeyé bacuró
  Sara yeyé bacuró...

(This prayer is said when someone is threatened with physical harm, knifewounds, stabbing etc.)

Ochosi.

Moforibale is performed by lifting the left leg, bending it slightly and imitating the action of shooting an arrow with the hands.
Prayers or songs:

> Ochosi de Mata
> Ilandá, oque, oque.
> Ochosi de Mata
> Ilandá, oque, oque.

Or:

> Ochosi aqui-lo-dara
> A la mata dé.
> Ochosi y de Mata;
> Oque, oque.
> Yambere ilora.
> Y de Mata;
> Oque, oque.

Osay, a *camino* of Obatalá.

There is only one prayer or song:

> Osay ilé ote-té
> Osay ilé ote-té
> Osay ilé ote-té
> Maribosay
> Maribosay
> Ñiqui, ñiqui beté
> Maribosay beté.

Obatalá.

He is invoked with the following phrase: Jecua Babá jecua!
Moforibale is performed lying face down on the floor and placing
the hands on the hips.
Songs or prayers:

> Babá furulo ere ooooh!
> Babá cañen ye-lé eribó.
> Ey! Iborere batibao,
> Erú ayé yagua ooooh!
> Eh, Baba-loro, leseccá.
> Eh, Baba-loro, leseccá.

Another:
> Eru ayace mimocheo.
> Eru ayé oche Babá!
> Si Obatalá tá cheré cheré.
> Como la iña cheyetó.
> Como la iña cheyetó.
> Babá oh... bá.
> Babá oh... bá.
> Oh... bá cheyetó.
> Oh... bá cheyetó.

And lastly:
> Agua tunaguarío
> Agua tunaguá
> Agua tunaguarío
> Agua tunaguá.
> Seculecun Baba-loro-qué

Agua tunaguá
A mi achó.

Changó.
(The first *"niño de la Simpatía"*)[2]
He is invoked by bowing ceremoniously before his altar, saying:
Cabiosile Changó!
Songs or prayers:

Moforibo-le-le
Moforibo-le-le
Changó topamolayé
Moforibo le-le, oooh!
Moforibo le-le, oooh!
Changó topamolayé.

Another:
Oh, baricoso, baricosooo…
Alardemí oooooh…
Alardó Cabo,
Alardemí oooooh!

Another:
Sibiriyó biriyó,
Sibiriyó biriyó.
Sibiriyó biralaguaaa,
Cabiosile Changó!

Another:
Lube, lube yombalá
Elube Changó eeeh

Elube amalá eeeh
Elube acucó eeeh
Elube oguedé eeeh
Elube acará eeeh
Elube obi eeeh

Another one:

Yemayá coroná
Yemayá coroná.
Changó lorisa,
Yemayá-n coroná...

And lastly:

Alardó Changó eh,
Eeeh, molelé.
Alardó Changó eh,
Eeeh, molelé

Ochún.
(The second *"niña de la simpatía."*)
She is invoked with the following words: Yalorde orí yeyeo, alber-
illí moró; iyá mío!
And when she "comes down," everyone cries: Yeyeo!
One of her songs or prayers:

Talardé yeyeo,
Talardé moró.
Yeyé talardé.
Babá talardé
Moró talardé.

And so on.

Another:

> Bi Ochun osuo
> Bi Ochun osuo.
> Tanima guá
> Iborere oooh
> Tanima guá
> Iborere oooh
> Eeeh, tanima guá
> iborereeeeee
> Talubo pití yeyeo
> Tanima guá
> iborereeeeee
> Talubo pití yeyeo,
> Umbo aquí yeyeo.

Another:

> Yeyé, yeyeo
> Adidé yu.
> Yeyé, yeyeo
> Adidé yú.
> Ariñale gua-gua-sí,
> Aqui vo yo.
> Otelera fá
> Adidé yú
> Ariñale gua-gua-si...

Another one:

> Tembelere iyá
> Tembelere iyá
> A bendere Ochun

Ochun chequeche
A bembe Ochun
Ochun panchagara.

And lastly:
Ochun yeyeo
Apetebí nombale
Ochun yeyeo
Apetebí nombale.
Yeyeo!
Dale coyú!
Yeyeo!

Yemayá.
(Third *"niña de la simpatía."*)
At the güemilere she is invoked by calling out: Oh, mío Yemayá!
To ask her to confer a power, one says: Yemayá Saramaguá, sayabí olocún…Iyá mío.
Here are some of her prayers or songs:

The first one:
Zacuta oñí oh,
Agua cesí
Egüí migdeeeeee
Dale Yaluma oooh
Yemayá aboyo, oooh
Egüí macedeeeee
Egdo mi deeeee

Another:
Yemayá umbo

A lo agua
Yemayá umbo
A lo agua.
Socum, socum, socum
Yemayá umbo
A lo agua
Oh, mío Yemayá!

Another:

Yemayá fumiloguó
Yemayá aaaaah
Yemayá fumiloguó.
Oñí Ochun.
Oñí lorisa.

Another:

Yemayá, Yemayá
Yemayá alardó.
Alardó a lo mío
A Saramaguá.
Iyá mío!
Zacuta, iyá mío.
Yemayá, Yemayá
Yemayá alardó.
Oh, lo mío!
Oh, lo mío!
Zacuta, iyá mío
Yemayá Saramaguá
Sayabí Olocún
Chiquití, iyá mío

Another one:

> Yemayá massó
> Quenqueré.
> Aboyó massó
> Quenqueré.
> Yemayá massó
> Quenqueré...

(this is repeated)

Lastly:

> Ucineba oooh!
> Aeeeeeee!
> Dale yaluma oooh
> Aboyó.
> Dale oñí abé
> Ayaba mío
> Ecoooooooo!
> Si Yemayá ta cuelé-cuelé
> Si Yemayá ta secú-secú.
> Aeeeeeeee!
> Dale yaluma oh,
> Dale ayaba mío, oñí abé
> Oh, mío Yemayá!

It is essential to end the ceremony with Eleguá.

The final, obligatory song:

> Coima coimani yacoima
> Coima coimani yacoima
> Coima coimani yacoima.

Eleguá nita laroye socúo eeeh!
Agó Eleguá eh!
Agó Elegúa eh!
Agó Eleguá eh!

The güemilere ends.

Vocabulary

Abure. Sister.

Aché. Power granted to the "saints" in order that they may exercise a particular power or possess someone.

Achó. Dress, clothing.

Acucó. Rooster.

Agayú Solá. Orisha corresponding to St Christopher of the Christian religion.

Aguanillí. The orisha Ogún is given this title in the prayers or songs of the Yoruba rites.

Aguardó. Grain of maize.

Álamo (*Ficus religiosia*, L.). Ornamental plant of the moraceae family. Very common in Cuba and frequently used in santería rituals. It originates from India.

Aleyo. Someone not initiated into santería. *Trans.*

Amalá. One of the dishes used in Yoruba rituals, made from maize meal and mutton.

Ardí-die. Hen.

Ardié-lé. Dove.

Babá. The orisha Obatalá is given this title in the prayers and songs of the güemilere.

Babalocha. Level of priesthood for men who have received the "collares" or necklaces of the "saint" at a ceremony in which they are granted the dispensation of officiating as true priests of the Yoruba cult.

Babalao. Rank conferred on the sons of St Francis, or, those who are deemed suitable for the dispensations of this saint considered a superior being in the hierarchy of the santería pseudoreligion. Only the babalao has the right to perform divination using the Ifá divining chain. The officiant should have absolute sexual integrity. A man who is weak-spirited may not receive the necklaces of St Francis.

Batá. Shoe.

Calabaza (Cucurbita maxima, L.). Plant of the cucurbitaceae family that is much used in our cuisine.

Caminos. For the santero, this term refers to the incidents and actions of an orisha at a particular juncture of their life. It acts as a perpetual reminder that can be produced at any time as required. Thus there are orishas who in their mythical lives were cowardly or brave, passionate lovers etc. When they possess a primed subject (babalocha or iyalocha) they may behave in a way that recalls some of these episodes from their lives.

Cascarilla. Eggshell that has been ground to a fine powder. Santeros say it protects us from death.

Ceiba. Tree sacred to those who practice santería. *Trans.*

Changó. A corruption of "Shangó," the African orisha. He corresponds to St Barbara in the Catholic religion. He is hermaphrodite. Santeros attribute this biological state to the "saint's" ability to "come through different caminos." However, a member of the female sex is denied the power to officiate in Changó's name though she may receive his dispensations.

Cofiadeno. Expresses a calm and tranquil state.

Di-logún. Mollusc shells used for divination by babalochas and iyalochas.

Echú or *Exú*. The Devil, evil spirit, a transmutation of Eleguá or Elegbá.

Ecrú-Aró. Type of pancake made with "carita" beans.

Ekuelé or *Ékuele*. Divining chain. *Trans*.

Ekuelé, tablero de. Round wooden board on which the divining chain is thrown.

Eleguá or *Elegbá*. Corresponds to the Lonely Soul of the Catholic religion. He transmutes into Echú, the Devil, though it would be wrong to consider him a deity that causes evil, rather, he is essential for all santería works, both good and evil. In santero slang, he is called the "concierge" or "the man behind the door" because he must be invoked at the beginning and end of religious celebrations, and also because santeros keep his amulet— normally a rough stone—hidden in a kind of cupboard behind the door, underneath the altar of the saint they worship.

Embó. This word refers to the preparation of an amulet, using some object belonging to the person for whom the spell (good or evil) is intended, such as items of clothing, jewelry, everyday items etc. Embó are also made from foodstuffs and aromatic plants with medicinal properties.

Emí. Cry for greeting Changó in his camino of drummer.

Epo. Shea butter.

Güemilere. Also known as batá or bembe, party at which Yoruba ritual is celebrated.

Icú. Materialization of Death.

Ifá, collar de. Necklace made of glass beads used by the *santero* to carry out his investigations before the proselyte. One may assume that when they speak of the collar del ekuelé they mean

this divining chain, which is most commonly used in the practices of the babalao.

Ilé. House, room.

Iyá mío! Cry meaning "my son!" [It actually means "my wife."
Trans.]

Iyare. Mother.

Moforibale. The action of greeting or showing respect to the
orisha. Moforibale is performed in a different way for each
saint. It often represents a particular activity that is associated
with them. All the santeros are obliged to perform moforibale to
the babalaos, hence the song:

    Orúmbila talardé
    Babá moforibale.

Moquenquen. Child.

Moquenqueré. Plural of *moquenquen.*

Ñame (Discore alata, L.). The "yellow yam," also known as
smooth or Guinea yam, because it was brought from that part of
Africa. It is a common food in Cuba.

Naná Bacurú. Corresponds to the Virgin of Mount Carmel in the
Catholic religion.

Oba. The santeros I interviewed recounted her legend but did not
tell me or did not know the Catholic saint to whom she corresponds.

Obatalá. Corresponds to the Virgin of Mercy. A hermaphrodite. In
the camino of Osan-quiriñán, God Himself. Some consider him
the most senior deity in the religion. He is the "owner of the

heads," that is, his proselytes may receive any saint.

Obeyes. Twins. They correspond to Saint Cosmas and Saint Damian. They are said to be the children of Ochún and Changó and are used quite frequently in santería works.

Obi. The fruit of the coconut palm (*Coco micifera, L.*). It is often used in divination rituals. The priest or priestess divides the fleshy, dried fruit into four pieces and throws them onto the ground, murmuring the word aché and observing the different positions in which the pieces fall, with the white side of the fruit showing or not. These positions are called *Alafia* (heaven and earth), which predicts good luck; *Icú*, certain death; *Monigue*, certainty in all matters; *Estague* (meaning unknown to me); and *Ocana-sorde*, which means the presence of the Devil (Echú). The following diagram shows the different combinations that may arise in this form of divination.

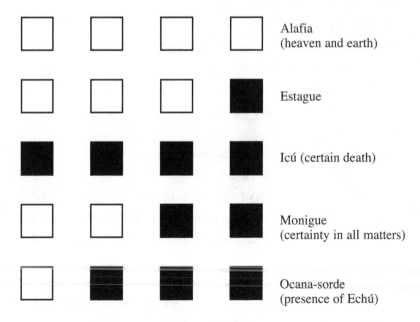

The black squares represent the husk of the coconut and the white squares the fleshy part of the fruit.

Obiní. Man. [It actually means "woman." *Trans.*]

Ochosi de Mata. Corresponds to Saint Norbert. He is a hunter. He was too unlucky in legend and memory to be used in santería works.

Ochun or *Oshun.* An important orisha, a high-ranking deity. She is the most important saint in Cuba, especially in areas where blacks are concentrated with the exception of Santiago de Cuba. There, perhaps because of the proximity of the Sanctuary of her namesake, the Virgin of Charity of El Cobre, Catholics have managed to preserve the traditions of this advocation of the Holy Virgin more or less intact. The santeros have had to channel their powerful superstitious and animistic energies into the worship of the orisha Babalú-Ayé (Saint Lazarus). In Havana, she is extremely popular. She represents love and her legends are full of scenes of passion.

Odu-dúa. The Holy Sacrament.

Oguedé. Bananas. *Trans.*

Ogún. An important orisha. He corresponds to Saint Peter. In his "camino" they call him "Ogún the Warrior," "Ogún Valenyo" when he is regarded as the metalworking king, and "Ogún Arere" when he is the farmer, "lord" of all the forests.

Oguó. Money.

Olelé. Pancake made from cornflour, sugar and milk.

Olofi. "Father" of heaven and earth. Perhaps because the social norms of today perceive women as inferior to men, santeros frequently use his name in their practices, confusing him with the universal god and obscuring the name of Oludummare, who is the mother of heaven and earth and has the same rank.

Oludummare. "Mother" of heaven and earth.

Omó. This term is used to refer to a woman who has never had a man. [It actually means "child." *Trans.*]

Omordé. Woman, in the specific sense of the word.

Omoyú lele-lepé. A saying that means "watch and remain silent."

Oñí. Honey.

Ondocó. Sexual contact.

Orí. Cocoa butter.

Oribule. Action of sleeping.

Orisaoco or *Orisha-Oco*. He corresponds to Saint Isidore the Farmer, as in the legend telling how he disappeared from active life. He is rarely called upon in santería works.

Orúmbila. He corresponds to Saint Francis. He is an important orisha. The santeros believe he is God's Secretary.

Osan-quiriñán (camino). When Obatalá appears in this camino he is considered to be Olofi himself.

Osay. He corresponds to Saint Joseph; some link him with Saint Benedict. I consider the first identification to be the more correct. He is believed to be a camino of Obatalá. This orisha seems to be the incarnation of santería pharmacology as he is considered the lord of all medicinal plants. He is a warrior.

Otí. Liquor. *Trans*.

Oyá. The mistress of the cemetery. She corresponds to the Virgin of Candlemas when she appears in the camino of Yanza. Others believe she is the Virgin of Mount Carmel and they identify Naná Bacurú with Saint Emilius, the patron saint of earthquakes.

Palma (Royal palm) (*Roystonea regia, H.B.K*). Plant of the palmaceae family. It is very common in Cuba and has an attractive appearance. Santeros say that Changó and Agayú Solá take shelter there.

Plátano (*Musa paradisiaca, L.*). Plant of the musaceae family, commonlyin Cuba.

Quimbombó (*Hibicus esculentus, L.*). Okra. Of the family of mal-
vaceae, it produces a viscous, grooved and pyramid-shaped
fruit that is used a great deal in Cuban the cuisine. It is of
African origin.

Registrar. To go for a consultation; the action of visiting a
babalao, babalocha or yalocha to make an enquiry, petition or
be granted spiritual or material relief.

Santería. In its pejorative sense: *brujería* or witchcraft. This term
refers to the Yoruba cult which was distorted when it became
diluted by a superior religion like Catholicism. It has, up to a
point, maintained its primitive purity because of the fundamental root of all religions: superstition. For this reason, I do not
believe blacks, in the time of submission, were converted to
Catholicism by means of violence but rather on account of his
enormous store of superstition. He has matched his animistic
beliefs with Catholicism, maintaining them in perfect harmony.
Saramaguá. Title given to Yemayá in the prayers or songs and
invocations of santería ritual.

Yalocha. Daughter of the "saint." This hierararchy is restricted to
females.
Yalorde! Exclamation used to implore Ochún in the songs and
prayers of the güemilere.
Yemayá. An important orisha. She corresponds to the Virgin of
Regla. She is said to be Ochún's younger sister. She is one of
the major orishas. She is hermaphrodite. She has a "camino"
called Olocún, a "strong saint" who is male and must be danced
wearing a mask adorned with seashells. There is a legend that

some who danced him were overcome by such violent shaking that they died instantly. Another of her caminos is Zacuta.

Yemayá Saramaguá. Name given to Yemayá in the prayers and songs of santería ritual.

Yibona. When someone is going to initiate into santería they are attended by an old woman who is an expert in these matters. She is called yibona and the initiate is called iyaguó.

Notes

1. *Brujería*: literally "witchcraft, sorcery," formerly used to denote Cuban religious practices of African origin, in particular, *santería.*
2. I.e. the most important "saints." Along with Ochún and Yemayá, he forms the Holy Trinity of santería. *Trans.*

About the Contributors

RÓMULO LACHATAÑERÉ stands alongside Fernando Ortiz and Lydia Cabrera as one of the pioneers of Afro-Cuban studies. He was also the first black Cuban intellectual to write extensively on the subject. Born in 1909 in Oriente Province, Lachatañeré was of Haitian ancestry and the grandson of Flor Crombet, one of the heroes of the wars of independence against Spain. He spent his early years in Santiago de Cuba, moving to Havana in 1926 to study at the university. He graduated in pharmacy three years later and remained in Havana, working in the laboratory of the Institute for Venereal Diseases.

While in Havana, Lachatañeré began to visit practitioners of *santería*, also known as the Lucumí religion, collecting and later publishing some of its myths. In 1937, he was listed as one of the founding members of the Sociedad de Estudios Afrocubanos, which had Fernando Ortiz as its president. From his position within the Afro-Cuban studies establishment, Lachatañeré was openly critical of existing "anthropological" research. This was because it had used Afro-Cubans as subjects for speculations on criminality and denigrated their religion by calling it *brujería* (witchcraft). However, despite his role in refocusing the research agenda towards the full spectrum of the Afro-Cuban experience and the centrality of its contribution to Cuban culture, Lachatañeré's work did not gain the recognition it deserved. Like his friend, the Afro-Cuban poet Nicolás Guillén, Lachatañeré was a member of the Communist party. His political activities during those turbulent times landed him in jail and led to the loss of his job. He was forced to return to Santiago. His book, *Oh mío Yemayá: Cuentos y cantos negros* (1938), was published in Manzanillo. Based on research in Havana, this was the first scholarly description of the mythology and ritual of *santería*.

Lachatañeré left for the U.S. in 1939. He continued to publish in Cuba and a series of articles, entitled *El sistema religioso de los lucumí y otras influencias africanas en Cuba*, appeared in the journal *Estudios Afrocubanos*. His second book, *Manual de Santería: El sistema de cul-*

tos "*lucumís*" (1942), was printed in Havana by a Communist-owned press. This was the first publication to examine *santería* as a religious system. It was intended as a corrective to previous studies that had misrepresented and trivialized the religious practices, ignoring the views of Afro-Cubans themselves. In the preface, Lachatañeré acknowledges the encouragement of important scholars in the field, including Ortiz, Melville Herskovits, Ruth Benedict, and William Bascom. Further articles on Afro-Cuban themes were published in a number of New York journals. In 1943–44, Lachatañeré enrolled in the U.S. Army, serving in Charleston Naval Hospital. Upon his return to civilian life, he worked in the laboratories of New York hospitals. In his spare time, he continued researching Afro-Caribbean traditions and studied photography. It was on his return from a field trip to Puerto Rico in 1952 that he died in a plane crash.

JORGE CASTELLANOS, born in Guantánamo in 1915, is one of the leading scholars of Cuban literature, history, and ethnography. He taught at the University of Santiago de Cuba and Marygrove College in Detroit, Michigan. His publications include *Tierra y Nación* [Land and Nation] (1955), *La Abolición de la Esclavitud en Popayán* [The Abolition of Slavery in Popayán] (1980), *Plácido, poeta social y político* [Plácido, Social and Political Poet] (1984), *24 de Febrero: un programa vigente* [February 24: An Ongoing Program] (1995), *Bitácora del Exilio* [Binnacle of Exile] (1999), *Invención Poética de la Nación Cubana* [Poetic Invention of the Cuban Nation] (2002), *Pioneros de la Etnografía Afrocubana* [Pioneers of Afro-Cuban Ethnography] (2003), and, with his daughter Isabel, the comprehensive four-volume work *Cultura Afrocubana* (1988–94). He has also published numerous articles on historical and literary themes in various journals and magazines. He is currently preparing a volume entitled *Encuentro en 1898* [Encounter in 1898] on the Spanish-Cuban-American War.

CHRISTINE AYORINDE, Ph.D., has spent many years visiting Cuba, researching and writing on Afro-Cuban themes, religion and questions of national identity. She is the translator of *Afro-Cuban Religions,* by Miguel Barnet, and *Cuban Legends,* edited by Salvador Bueno. Her publications include *Afro-Cuban Religiosity, Revolution and National Identity* (2004) and chapters in *Identity in the Shadow of Slavery* (2000), *The Yoruba Diaspora in the Atlantic World* (2005), and *Contesting Freedom: Control and Resistance in the Century after Emancipation in the Caribbean* (2005).

SIEGFRIED KADEN is a painter and lecturer in fine arts. His work has been exhibited and collected by a number of major European museums, including the Munich Lenbachhaus (Museum of Contemporary Art), the Stuttgart Hospitalhof, the City of Heidelberg Museum, the Malaga Museum of Fine Arts, the Palacio de la Madraza in Granada (Spain), the Fundación Ludwig de Cuba in Havana, and the Goethe Institutes in Rotterdam and Madrid. He has held over fifty individual shows and numerous group exhibitions at major galleries and art fairs in Cuba, Spain, Switzerland, the Netherlands, and Germany. Exhibition catalogues have been published in Spain, Switzerland, Germany, and Austria. He has received numerous awards, including gold medals from the University of Vienna, the cities of Munich, Germany, and Mulhouse, Switzerland, the National Award of the State of Bavaria, and the Frankfurt International Book Fair. Specialist magazines such as *Art in America, ART,* and *Kunstforum International* have reviewed his work and it has been featured on public television programs in Cuba and Germany. He is the co-author and illustrator of eight books and films, including *Hannibal* (animation, 1988), *War Games* (1995), *Little Hippology* (1996), and *Silent Days in Havana* (1999). He has taught at the Academy of Arts, Mannheim, the University of Weimar, and the University of Irsee in Germany, at the Cuban Instituto Superior de las Artes Plásticas, and at the Escuela de Bellas Artes, San Alejandro, Havana. He organized major international art exhibitions in Havana in 2003 and 2004.

Printed in the USA
CPSIA information can be obtained
at www.ICGtesting.com
JSHW081651121023
49862JS00002B/83